Facts That Last
Subtraction

A Balanced Approach
to Memorization

Larry Leutzinger

Creative Publications®
A Tribune Education Company

Acknowledgments

Contributing Writers Janet Pittock, Jeffrey Stiegel

Editor Diane Nieker

Creative Director Karen Lee

Design Gerta Sorensen

Cover Illustration Amanda Haley

Illustrators Sarah Frederking, Tammie Lyon

Production Carlisle Communications, Ltd.

ISBN 0-7622-1212-8

Catalog No. 32311

Customer Service 800-624-0822

http://www.creativepublications.com

1 2 3 4 5 6 7 8 ML 05 04 03 02 01 00 99

Contents

Introduction

Teaching basic facts is an important component of any successful mathematics program. Many of the recommendations made by the National Council of Teachers of Mathematics (NCTM) in their 1989 *Standards* assume children have fluency with basic operations. Mastery of this information is necessary for developing both mental math and estimation skills. Many mathematical tasks become more efficient when basic facts can be recalled quickly and accurately.

In the past, teaching basic facts was often over-emphasized with too much time devoted to repetitive practice. The seven subtraction strategies presented in this book will help children remember their facts with a more appropriate amount of practice. The activities in *Facts That Last* provide the central portion of a successful three-step sequence for mastering basic facts.

Having an understanding of number and the basic concepts of subtraction is the first step in the process of mastering the basic facts. (See prerequisites beginning on page vi.) The contents of this book address the second step—learning fact strategies to facilitate recall. Finally, children need to keep facts "fresh" with an appropriate amount of continuing practice. Practice can come from working on isolated facts or from working with facts embedded in more complex activities.

The strategies in this book demonstrate how to organize facts into groups that can be handled with generalizations. With this knowledge, the effort of learning each of 121 subtraction facts is reduced to the ease of remembering a handful of strategies. Mathematically powerful children often use many of these strategies naturally. When you encourage children in your class to use and discuss these strategies, you make that power available to your entire class!

The seven subtraction strategies presented in this book include count back, count up, fact families, think addition, patterns, subtracting from ten, and ten-between. A chart listing the strategies can be found on the next page.

Strategy Chart

Count Back

When subtracting 0, 1, 2, or 3, count back from the minuend. For example, with 12 − 3, start at the minuend 12, and count back three numbers, 11, 10, 9. Thus 12 − 3 = 9.

Count Up

If two numbers are close together, count up from the number to be subtracted. For example, with 11 − 8, start at eight and count up 9, 10, 11. Three numbers are counted, so 11 − 8 = 3.

Fact Families

Fact-families are groups of two or four related addition and subtraction facts. For example, 1 + 2 = 3, 2 + 1 = 3, 3 − 1 = 2, and 3 − 2 = 1 are four facts in one fact family.

Think Addition

To find the difference for a subtraction fact, think of the related addition fact. For example, for 8 − 3 = ?, think 3 + ? = 8. Since 3 + 5 = 8, 8 − 3 = 5.

Patterns

Some facts become easy to remember because they follow a pattern. For example, any number minus itself is always equal to zero.

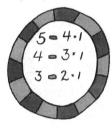

Subtract from Ten

This strategy involves visualizing the removal of counters from a ten-frame.

Ten Between

When the number ten lies between the two numbers of the subtraction fact, find the distance from ten for each of the numbers, then add their distances together. For example, with 13 − 8, 13 is 3 away from 10, 8 is 2 away from 10, and since 2 + 3 = 5, 13 − 8 = 5.

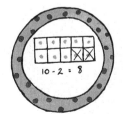

How This Book Is Organized

How to Use This Book

Facts That Last combines lessons that present the strategies and practice children need to memorize their facts. You may choose to supplement or replace the work in your mathematics textbook with this material. You may choose to use the entire book, or to teach only those strategies you feel will provide the most benefit to your students.

For purposes of clarity, throughout this book the term *minuend* will be used to describe the number from which an amount is being subtracted, the term *subtrahend* will be used to describe the amount being subtracted, and the term *difference* will describe the result of the subtraction.

$$
\begin{array}{r}
15 \\
- \quad 7 \\
\hline
8
\end{array}
\quad
\begin{array}{l}
\text{minuend} \\
\text{subtrahend} \\
\text{difference}
\end{array}
$$

A reproducible version of the subtraction chart used in this book can be found on page 84. To use the chart, first locate the minuend in the column at the left. Next, find the subtrahend along the right side of the chart. Read down the diagonal column from the subtrahend to the row of the minuend to get to the difference. The simplified chart below highlights the fact $5 - 3 = 2$.

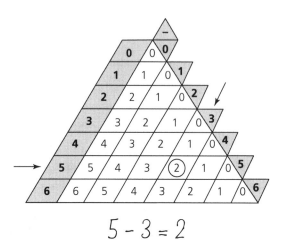

$$5 - 3 = 2$$

Teaching Sequence

First, determine that your children are ready to memorize. The prerequisites chart (pages viii-1) lists evidences of readiness. Should you conclude that children are not ready, refer to the activities and resources listed in the chart for additional experiences.

At the beginning of each strategy section you'll find an overview that provides a summary of the strategy, prerequisites specific to that strategy, information about when to use the strategy, and additional strategy-related experiences for your students. You'll also find references to the optional practice workbook.

Every strategy section starts with warm-ups. Warm-ups include introductory experiences, mental math experiences, and a refreshing of the skills children need for the strategy. These warm-ups take about three to five minutes. Some strategy sections have five warm-ups while others have ten. Many teachers enjoy using these warm-ups during the transition time between activities or when children are lining up.

Next comes an activity designed to give children experience and practice with the strategy. Activities may be done with the whole class, in cooperative groups, or individually. Each activity takes at least one class period.

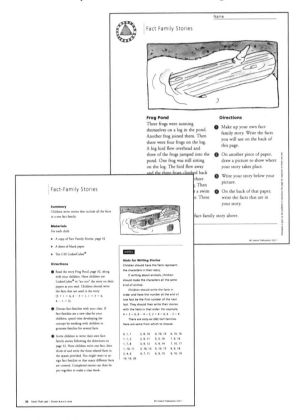

The third component of each strategy section is practice. Practices are similar in format and feel to the warm-ups. The aim of practice is to have children use the strategy to recall facts quickly and correctly.

Once the children in your class have memorized their subtraction facts, you can help them to maintain quick and accurate recall by providing engaging ways to practice those facts. See the bibliography (page 88) for complete information about suggested resources.

Talk About It

Children who discuss their thinking and hear how other children think become stronger at using strategies. Throughout the book you'll find hints for leading discourse with children about their thinking. Often, questions for a class discussion will appear at the beginning of a set of warm-ups or practice pages. These questions are designed to be used throughout the warm-up or practice period. You'll also find questions asking children to describe their thinking embedded in the activities.

Materials

Teacher notes found at the beginning of activities, warm-ups, and practice sets tell you what supplies are needed for the activity. The items listed, however, are by no means the only materials that can be used. If you don't have the specific equipment named, use alternative materials that are available to you. Material lists for some of the activities offer suggestions for alternatives.

The following is a list of all of the materials suggested for use with activities in this book.

▶ Twenty (20) LinkerCubes® for each child

▶ A balance scale

▶ Three (3) blank cubes for each pair of children

▶ Ten (10) two-color beans for each group of four children

▶ Number cards 0 through 100

▶ Addition and subtraction flash cards

Additional Materials

Eight (8) plastic margarine tubs or small plastic bowls

Prerequisites

Research shows that children with a solid conceptual understanding of an operation are more successful memorizing their facts. The following chart summarizes key concepts that students should fully understand before they are asked to begin memorizing facts. If your children own the concepts listed in the first column of the chart, they are ready to begin successfully committing their facts to memory. However, if you determine that your students need more experiences before they begin the activities in this book, you might start with the suggestions offered in the second column of the chart. Additional activities can be found in the resources listed in the third column. A full bibliography is located on page 88.

Key Concepts

Children explain that one model of subtraction is taking items away. They can model subtraction problems with drawings, cubes, or other manipulatives.

Children explain that one model of subtraction is comparing two groups to find the difference. They can model this with manipulatives.

Children employ various methods to arrive at the correct answers to subtraction facts. Methods may include counting on fingers, using manipulatives, counting up, relating a fact to another fact that is similar, and using number sense to find the answer.

Children understand relationships of numbers from zero (0) to twenty (20). Given two numbers under twenty (20), children immediately know which number is greater than or less than the other.

Children are fluent with their addition facts.

Children demonstrate understanding of the relationship between addition and subtraction.

Activities to Provide More Experiences	**Recommended Resources**

Relate a situation that can be described with a subtraction fact. Have children make a drawing to illustrate the situation.

This might be a child's representation of what happens when 3 of 7 birds fly out of the tree.

$$7 - 3 = 4$$

Constructing Ideas About Number Combinations by Sandra Ward.

Understanding Addition & Subtraction by Linda Holden and Micaelia Randolph Brummett.

Ask children to build LinkerCube® towers of different lengths, compare the two towers, and tell the subtraction fact that describes the difference between the number of cubes in the towers.

$$5 - 2 = 3$$

Constructing Ideas About Number Combinations by Sandra Ward.

Understanding Addition & Subtraction by Linda Holden and Micaelia Randolph Brummett.

Provide additional experiences for children to find answers for situations involving subtraction. In whole class discussions, encourage children to tell how they figure out answers when they do not have facts memorized.

Smart Arithmetic, Grades 1–3 by Rhea Irvine and Kathryn Walker.

Dictate two numbers and have children point to the numbers on a number line. Ask children to tell you which number is greater. On another pair of numbers, have children tell you which is less.

7 8 9 10 11 12 13 14 15 16

Smart Arithmetic, Grades 1–3 by Rhea Irvine and Kathryn Walker.

Have children use an addition chart to tell you about any patterns they notice. Lead a class discussion in which children share their method(s) for remembering their facts.

Facts That Last: A Balanced Approach to Addition Fact Memorization by Larry Leutzinger.

Practice Worth Repeating: Activities, Puzzles, and Games for Addition Facts by Janet Pittock and Ann Roper.

Use two colors of LinkerCubes® to model an addition fact, for example 3 + 2. Ask children to tell you the addition fact. Then ask them to tell you how much 5 − 3 is and how they know. Repeat this activity until it is easy for children to see all four facts in this fact family.

Constructing Ideas About Number Combinations by Sandra Ward.

Count-back Strategy Overview

What is the Count-back Strategy?

The count-back strategy is one that many children use naturally. They simply count back the number being subtracted. For example, with 8 − 3, think or say 8, then count back three. Eight—7, 6, 5. So 8 − 3 = 5.

When to Use the Count-back Strategy

The count-back strategy is best used when subtracting zero, one, two, or three.

Prerequisites

Children should understand subtraction concepts (pages vi–vii). They should also be fluent at counting backwards when starting from twenty or less.

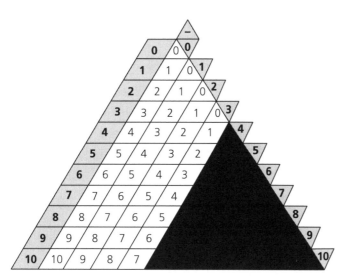

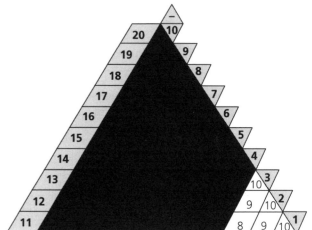

Additional Experiences

Label eight small plastic margarine tubs both inside and out with the numbers 5 through 12. If using this as a small group activity, try to limit the group to four children. Assign one tub per child. Have children make groups of LinkerCubes® according to the labels in their tubs, then invert the tubs and place them over the cubes. The bowl will serve as a "hive" for the LinkerCubes "bees."

Write "−1," "−2," and "−3" on blank cards using a separate card for each number. Hold up a card and instruct children to remove the number of bees indicated by the card from their hives. Children should count back as the bees leave the hive. For example, if a hive is labeled "5" and the card reads "−3," a child would remove three bees, one at a time, and say "4, 3, 2. 5 − 3 = 2."

Additional practice can be found in *Practice Your Facts, Levels 1–5,* by Creative Publications.

Count-back Strategy

Warm-ups

Each warm-up exercise set should take two (2) or three (3) minutes. The short exercise sets are great for filling transition times. Some teachers use them while children stand in line.

Materials

Number cards 0 through 100

Talk About It

As the children work through these warm-ups, ask them to talk about their thinking. This not only helps you assess, but gives children a chance to clarify their thinking and to hear about ways of thinking that might be different from theirs. You might ask questions like

As you count back, how do you keep track of the numbers to be sure you count correctly?
(Answers will vary.)

Do you count the number you are counting back from as the first number when you are counting back?
(No.)

Day 1

Show a number card, for example 6.

Count back (0 or 1).

What is the result?
(6 or 5)

Show number cards 1 through 10. Each card should be shown at least once.

Extension Use number cards 11 through 99. Have children count back 0 or 1.

Day 2

Show a number card, for example 4.

Show this number of fingers on your hand(s).

Count back (0 or 1) fingers.

How many fingers are still showing?
(4 or 3)

Show number cards 1 through 10. Each card should be shown at least once.

Extension Use number cards 11 through 20. Have children count back 0 or 1 fingers.

Day 3

Show a number card, for example 7.

Count back 2 from the number you see.

What is the result?
(5)

Show number cards 2 through 10. Each card should be shown at least once.

Extension Use number cards 11 through 99. Have children count back 2.

Day 4

Show a number card, for example 9.

Show this number of fingers on your hand(s).

Count back 2 fingers.

How many fingers are still showing?
(7)

Show number cards 2 through 10. Each card should be shown at least once.

Extension Use number cards 12 through 20. Have children count back 2 fingers.

Day 5

Show a number card, for example 5.

Count back 3 from the number you see.

What is the result?
(2)

Show number cards 3 through 10. Each card should be shown at least once.

Extension Use number cards 11 through 99. Have children count back three.

Day 6

Show a number card, for example 7.

Show this number of fingers on your hand(s).

Count back 3 fingers.

How many fingers are still showing?
(4)

Show number cards 3 through 10. Each card should be shown at least once.

Extension Use number cards 13 through 20. Have children count back 3 fingers.

Day 7

Show a number card, for example 10.

Count back (2 or 3).

What is the result?
(8 or 7)

Show number cards 2 through 10. Each card should be shown at least once.

Extension Use number cards 11 through 99. Have children count back 2 or 3.

Day 8

Show a number card, for example 3.

Show this number of fingers on your hand(s).

Count back (2 or 3) fingers.

How many fingers are still showing?
(1 or 0)

Show number cards 2 through 10. Each card should be shown at least once.

Extension Use number cards 12 through 20. Have children count back 2 or 3 fingers.

Day 9

Show children a number card, for example 6.

Count back
(0, 1, 2, or 3)

What is the result?
(6, 5, 4, or 3)

Use number cards 1 through 10. Have children count back different amounts for each number as time allows for each.

Extension Use number cards 11 through 99. Have children count back 0, 1, 2, or 3.

Day 10

Show a number card, for example 4.

Count back (0, 1, 2, or 3).

What is the result?
(4, 3, 2, or 1)

Show number cards 1 through 10. Each card should be shown at least once.

Extension Use number cards from 11 through 99. Have children count back 0, 1, 2, or 3.

Count Back Call-out

Whole Class Activity

Summary
This is a class round-robin activity. When a number is called out, children count back two to find the difference. The child holding the number corresponding to the difference indicates he or she has the number, states the fact, then calls out the next number.

Materials
A set of the call-out cards on page 9

Preparation
Make a copy of page 9 and cut cards apart. Distribute cards in random order. Note that for this set of twenty-five cards, the first response is 7. The last call-out number, 11, will have a response of 9 and will bring play back to you.

Directions

❶ Instruct children to listen carefully to each call-out number and then count back two from that number. The child with the number that is two less than the call-out number in the center of his or her card will answer with the number.

❷ Begin the game by calling out the first number, 9. "The call-out number is 9."

❸ Tell children to check their cards. The child holding the card with 7 in the center should announce, "9 − 2 = 7. I have 7."

❹ That child calls out the number located at the bottom of his or her card.

❺ Have children continue to count back and call out numbers until 11 is called out, bringing the response back to you. Announce that 11 − 2 = 9, that you have 9, and end the game.

Extension or Homework
Make a copy of Mystery Cards, pages 10 and 11, for each child. Have children follow directions on page 10 to make three sets of cards, each with its own rule. Cards with lines have a difference of one, those with triangles have a difference of two, and those with circles have a difference of three. When they've figured out the rule for a set, children can look at one side of a card from the set and know what number is on the opposite side.

tips for playing If you have extra call-out cards, give some students two.

If needed, make additional cards. Discard the last card on the page (24 in center) and make a new card with 24 in the center. Make the call-out number on new cards 30 or greater. The center response number of each subsequent card should be two less than the last call out used. On the very last card you make, have the call-out number be 11 so the play returns to you for a response of 9 to end the game.

I have 13 — call out 23	I have 22 — call out 6	I have 25 — call out 7	I have 17 — call out 8	I have 24 — call out 11
I have 2 — call out 15	I have 3 — call out 24	I have 19 — call out 27	I have 11 — call out 19	I have 8 — call out 26
I have 18 — call out 4	I have 15 — call out 5	I have 26 — call out 21	I have 23 — call out 13	I have 12 — call out 10
I have 10 — call out 20	I have 1 — call out 17	I have 16 — call out 28	I have 14 — call out 25	I have 20 — call out 14
I have 7 — call out 12	I have 21 — call out 3	I have 4 — call out 18	I have 5 — call out 16	I have 6 — call out 22

Mystery Cards Part 1

Once you know the secret, you'll be able to tell what number is on the other side of a mystery card before looking. Can you figure out how the cards work?

Directions

1 Fold page 11 in half along the solid fold line. Open the paper and put glue on the blank side. Press glued sides together. Allow glue to dry.

2 Cut along the dotted lines. Separate cards into three groups—circles, lines, and those with triangles.

3 Each group has a different rule. If you know the rule, you will be able to tell what number is on the other side of the card. Figure out the rule for each set and write the rules here.

Challenge Make more cards for each set. Make a new set of cards with a different rule.

Rule for cards with lines

_____

_____

Rule for cards with circles

_____

_____

Rule for cards with triangles

_____

_____

Mystery Cards Part 2

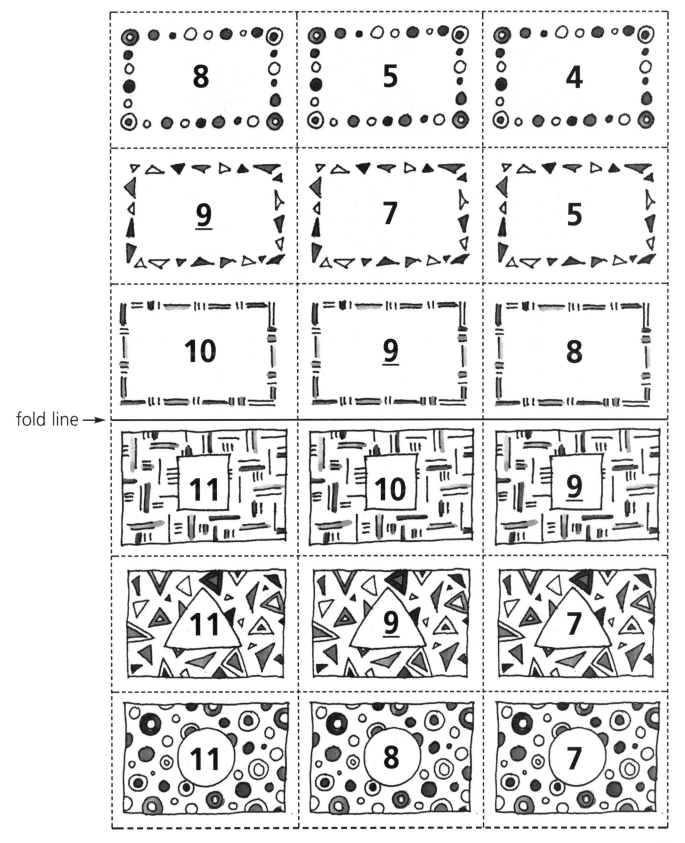

fold line →

Count-back Strategy

Practice

Work on these sets of practice exercises until children can get each answer within three (3) seconds. Ask children to say or write the entire fact rather than just the answer. Present the facts in various ways. Have children listen and then reply verbally, or use flash cards and have the children write their facts. Varying the format helps all children focus on the facts.

Talk About It

Encourage children to tell you about their thinking. Ask questions like

What do you know about subtracting zero?
(Any number minus zero is that number.)

Why does that rule work?
(It works because zero means "none.")

What do you know about subtracting one?
(Any number minus one is the counting number that comes before the number.)

What do you know about subtracting two?
(You count back two. Also, counting back two from any even number produces the previous even number. Counting back two from an odd number produces the previous odd number.)

What do you know about subtracting three?
(You count back three.)

Day 1

Present these facts.

7 − 0 (7)	7 − 1 (6)
5 − 1 (4)	3 − 0 (3)
1 − 0 (1)	8 − 0 (8)
4 − 1 (3)	1 − 1 (0)
8 − 1 (7)	0 − 0 (0)
6 − 0 (6)	2 − 1 (1)
2 − 0 (2)	5 − 0 (5)
10 − 1 (9)	6 − 1 (5)
4 − 0 (4)	10 − 0 (10)
3 − 1 (2)	9 − 1 (8)

Extension Subtract 0 or 1 from numbers through 99.

Day 2

Present these facts.

6 − 1 (5)	10 − 0 (10)
5 − 0 (5)	7 − 0 (7)
1 − 1 (0)	5 − 1 (4)
9 − 0 (9)	1 − 0 (1)
2 − 0 (2)	10 − 1 (9)
8 − 1 (7)	4 − 1 (3)
0 − 0 (0)	3 − 0 (3)
4 − 0 (4)	8 − 0 (8)
3 − 1 (2)	2 − 1 (1)
9 − 1 (8)	7 − 1 (6)

Extension Subtract 0 or 1 from numbers through 99.

Day 4

Present these facts.

7 − 2 (5)	4 − 2 (2)
5 − 0 (5)	10 − 1 (9)
3 − 2 (1)	8 − 2 (6)
8 − 1 (7)	0 − 0 (0)
6 − 2 (4)	3 − 0 (3)
10 − 0 (10)	2 − 2 (0)
3 − 1 (2)	10 − 2 (8)
9 − 2 (7)	8 − 0 (8)
7 − 1 (6)	5 − 2 (3)
1 − 0 (1)	9 − 1 (8)

Extension Subtract 0, 1, or 2 from numbers through 99.

Day 3

Present these facts.

8 − 2 (6)	9 − 0 (9)
5 − 1 (4)	4 − 2 (2)
6 − 0 (6)	6 − 1 (5)
5 − 2 (3)	7 − 2 (5)
9 − 1 (8)	2 − 0 (2)
2 − 2 (0)	3 − 2 (1)
6 − 2 (4)	4 − 1 (3)
4 − 0 (4)	7 − 0 (7)
2 − 1 (1)	9 − 2 (7)
10 − 2 (8)	1 − 1 (0)

Extension Subtract 0, 1, or 2 from numbers through 99.

Day 5

Present these facts.

7 − 3 (4)	9 − 3 (6)
8 − 2 (6)	3 − 2 (1)
4 − 3 (1)	2 − 1 (1)
6 − 1 (5)	5 − 3 (2)
4 − 0 (4)	6 − 0 (6)
10 − 3 (7)	3 − 3 (0)
5 − 2 (3)	7 − 2 (5)
6 − 3 (3)	8 − 3 (5)
4 − 1 (3)	9 − 2 (7)
7 − 0 (7)	8 − 1 (7)

Extension Subtract 0, 1, 2, or 3 from numbers through 99.

Day 7

Present these facts.

9 − 3 (6)	8 − 3 (5)
5 − 2 (3)	10 − 2 (8)
6 − 1 (5)	4 − 1 (3)
6 − 3 (3)	3 − 3 (0)
4 − 0 (4)	7 − 0 (7)
7 − 3 (4)	7 − 2 (5)
8 − 2 (6)	10 − 3 (7)
4 − 3 (1)	2 − 2 (0)
9 − 1 (8)	5 − 3 (2)
3 − 2 (1)	9 − 2 (7)

Extension Subtract 0, 1, 2, or 3 from numbers through 99.

Day 6

Present these facts.

5 − 3 (2)	5 − 1 (4)
10 − 2 (8)	3 − 3 (0)
7 − 1 (6)	4 − 2 (2)
8 − 3 (5)	9 − 0 (9)
3 − 0 (3)	9 − 1 (8)
4 − 3 (1)	10 − 3 (7)
6 − 2 (4)	2 − 2 (0)
3 − 1 (2)	7 − 3 (4)
9 − 3 (6)	8 − 0 (8)
2 − 0 (2)	6 − 3 (3)

Extension Subtract 0, 1, 2, or 3 from numbers through 99.

Day 8

Present these facts.

8 − 3 (5)	10 − 0 (10)
6 − 2 (4)	7 − 2 (5)
5 − 0 (5)	3 − 3 (0)
10 − 3 (7)	7 − 3 (4)
4 − 2 (2)	5 − 2 (3)
5 − 1 (4)	1 − 0 (1)
4 − 3 (1)	8 − 2 (6)
9 − 2 (7)	9 − 3 (6)
2 − 1 (1)	10 − 2 (8)
6 − 3 (3)	5 − 3 (2)

Extension Subtract 0, 1, 2, or 3 from numbers through 99.

Day 9

Present these facts.

8 − 1 (7)	8 − 0 (8)
6 − 0 (6)	5 − 2 (3)
7 − 3 (4)	6 − 3 (3)
3 − 2 (1)	4 − 0 (4)
9 − 3 (6)	9 − 2 (7)
1 − 1 (0)	3 − 1 (2)
0 − 0 (0)	10 − 3 (7)
8 − 2 (6)	7 − 1 (6)
10 − 1 (9)	5 − 0 (5)
4 − 3 (1)	6 − 2 (4)

Extension Subtract 0, 1, 2, or 3 from numbers through 99.

Day 10

Present these facts.

7 − 2 (5)	5 − 1 (4)
8 − 3 (5)	7 − 0 (7)
9 − 1 (8)	6 − 1 (5)
3 − 0 (3)	7 − 3 (4)
5 − 3 (2)	2 − 2 (0)
4 − 1 (3)	2 − 1 (1)
2 − 0 (2)	9 − 0 (9)
4 − 2 (2)	10 − 3 (7)
3 − 3 (0)	8 − 2 (6)
10 − 2 (8)	1 − 0 (1)

Extension Subtract 0, 1, 2, or 3 from numbers through 99.

Count-up Strategy Overview

What is the Count-up Strategy?

In using the count-up strategy, begin with the lesser number and keep track of how many numbers are counted up to get to the greater number. For example, for $11 - 9$, start at 9 and count 10, 11. Two numbers were counted, so $11 - 9 = 2$.

Prerequisites

Children should understand subtraction concepts (pages vi-vii). This strategy focuses on the idea of comparing two groups to find the difference.

When to Use the Count-up Strategy

Use the count-up strategy when the two numbers in the subtraction fact are no more than three numbers apart.

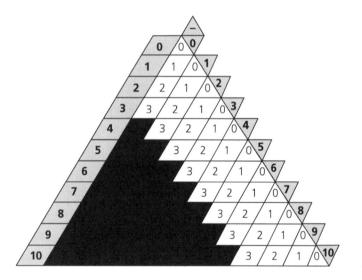

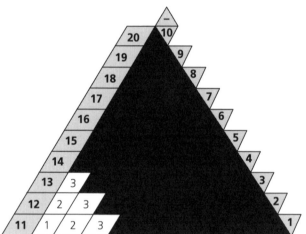

Additional Experiences

Use "line time" to reinforce count-up thinking. Have children form a line. Ask them to count off and ask each child to keep track of his or her number in line. Select one child to restate his or her number. Ask how many children are behind that child. Have children in back of the one selected count off while everyone keeps track of how many count off. You might have children raise their hands as they count off. If twelve children are in the line and you select the 9th child, he or she will say "9," and the children in back will count up 10, 11, 12. Since three children counted up, $12 - 9 = 3$.

Additional practice can be found in *Practice Your Facts, Levels 1–5,* by Creative Publications.

Count-up Strategy

Warm-ups

Each warm-up exercise set should take two (2) or three (3) minutes. The short exercise sets are great for filling transition times. Some teachers use them while children stand in line.

Materials

▶ Number cards 0–100

▶ Flash cards

Talk About It

As the children work through these warm-ups, ask them to talk about their thinking. This not only helps you assess, but gives children a chance to clarify their thinking and to hear about ways of thinking that might be different from theirs. You might ask questions like

How do you keep track of how many numbers you have counted up?
(Accept all reasonable explanations.)

How does counting up relate to subtraction facts?
(The difference between the two numbers in the subtraction fact is the same as the number counted up.)

How do you know which number to count up from in a subtraction problem?
(The number being subtracted, or taken away, is the one from which to count up.)

Does the number you are counting up from count as the first number when counting up?
(No.)

Day 1

Show children two number cards, for example 6 and 8.

Which number is (less or greater)?
Use number cards 0 through 12. Pair cards that have a difference of 1, 2, or 3.

Extension Use number cards 13 through 99. Pair cards that have a difference of 1, 2, or 3.

Day 2

Show a subtraction flash card with a difference of 1, 2, or 3.

Which number is (less or greater)?
Repeat until most children can recognize which is less or greater with ease.

Extension Ask

What do you notice about all of the subtraction facts on the flash cards?
(The lesser number is always being taken away from the greater number.)

Day 3

Show two number cards, for example 7 and 9.

Which number is less?

(7)

Count up to the greater number. How many numbers did you count?

(2)

Use number cards 0 through 12. Pair cards that have a difference of 1 or 2.

Extension Use number cards 13 through 99. Pair cards that have a difference of 1 or 2.

Day 4

Show two number cards, for example 9 and 12.

Which number is less?

(9)

Count up to the greater number. How many numbers did you count?

(3)

Use number cards 0 through 12. Pair cards that have a difference of 1, 2, or 3.

Extension Use number cards 13 through 99. Pair cards that have a difference of 1, 2, or 3.

Day 5

Show two number cards, for example 4 and 6.

Which number is less?

(4)

Count up to the greater number. How many numbers did you count?

(2)

Use number cards 0 through 12. Pair cards that have a difference of 1, 2, or 3.

Extension Use number cards 13 through 99. Pair cards that have a difference of 1, 2, or 3.

One, Two, or Three More?

Summary

Children are given a brief glimpse at a pair of LinkerCube® trains and asked to tell the difference in their lengths. Children then suggest lengths for each train in the pair.

Small Group Activity

Materials

Each pair of children needs

▶ Twenty (20) LinkerCubes®

▶ A copy of One, Two, or Three More, page 21

Preparation

If you use an overhead projector for this activity, make several pairs of LinkerCube® trains before presenting the activity. Allow a slight space between cubes rather than pressing them tightly together. This will allow children to "read" them more easily. Pairs of trains should have a difference of one, two, or three cubes.

An alternative would be to prepare simple drawings of trains on chart paper in advance of the activity. During the activity, cover each drawing until you are ready to flash it.

Directions

❶ Show one pair of trains. Allow a quick look so children get a chance to see the difference but do not have enough time to count the number of cubes in each train.

❷ Ask children to tell you the number difference between the two trains. Then ask children to tell you how long each train in the pair could be to have that difference. Write the number pairs offered on the board.

❸ Have students work in pairs to complete page 22.

> **notes** At some point during this activity children should begin to express the fact trains and their differences as subtraction sentences rather than number pairs. The timing will depend on your class. Some groups will describe the differences as subtraction early in the activity while other groups might require prompting to make this transition. The Talk About It section offers a good place to encourage subtraction language.

Talk About It

How did you figure out the difference between the two trains so quickly?
(Children may have a variety of answers for this and they find it interesting to hear the different methods used to complete the task.)

What are possible trains with differences of (1, 2, or 3)?
(Record answers on the board. Accept all reasonable answers.)

Have we listed all the possible train pairs? How do you know?
(Check by making an organized list. Use the pattern in the list to see if any pairs are missing.)

How did you figure out which pairs of trains were possible?
(Longer train – shorter train = 1 or 2 or 3. Accept all accurate responses.)

Did anyone have a different way to figure pairs of trains that would be possible?
(Choosing the smaller number and counting up, and choosing the larger number and counting back are two methods. Accept all accurate methods.)

Extension or Homework

Have children work in pairs. As they work through this activity, each pair will need a balance scale, twenty (20) LinkerCubes® and two pieces of paper. Each child will need one (1) copy of How Much More to Balance? page 23.

Demonstrate the proper way to set up the balance and discuss how to make the balance level by asking for and then testing suggestions from the children.

Each child should have an opportunity to use the balance while working on this activity.

One, Two, or Three More?

Make pairs of LinkerCube® trains with differences of 1, 2, or 3. How long should the trains be in each pair?

Directions

1 Make two LinkerCube® trains. Make one train 1, 2, or 3 cubes longer than the other. Do not let your partner see the trains as you make them.

2 Show the trains for about half a second.

3 Ask your partner to tell you how much longer one train is than the other. Write his or her answer in the table.

4 Have your partner guess how many cubes are in each train. Write his or her answers in the table. Together, count the cubes in each train and check the difference.

5 Take turns building trains and guessing.

How much longer	Longer train	Shorter train

How Much More to Balance?

How many LinkerCubes® must be added to make the balance level?

Directions

1 Place some LinkerCubes on one side of a balance while your partner covers his or her eyes. Write the number that tells how many cubes on a piece of paper. Cover the cubes with the paper.

2 Place two or three fewer cubes on the other side of the balance. Write the number that tells how many on another piece of paper and cover the cubes.

3 Write both numbers in the table.

4 Ask your partner to look and tell how many cubes he or she thinks need to be added to make the balance level. Write your partner's answer in the table under "Number you think will balance."

6 Check your partner's answer by adding the number of cubes he or she says are needed. Write the actual number of cubes needed in the table.

7 Take turns placing cubes, guessing numbers, and writing answers in the table.

Larger number	Smaller number	Number you think will balance	Actual number to balance

Count-up Strategy

Practice

Work on these sets of practice exercises until children can get each answer within three (3) seconds. Ask children to state the entire fact rather than just the answer. Stating the complete fact improves students' recall. Present the facts in various ways. Ask the children to listen and then reply verbally, or use flash cards and have the children write their facts. Varying the format helps all children focus on the facts.

Talk About It

Encourage children to talk about their thinking. Ask questions like

How are the numbers in a subtraction problem arranged?
(The minuend is written first in a horizontal presentation, on top in a vertical presentation. At this stage of children's learning, the minuend will be the greater of the two numbers.)

From which number do you begin counting up?
(The lesser number; the bottom number; or the number at the right, depending on presentation.)

Does this number count as the first number when counting up?
(No.)

Why don't you count up from the larger number?
(You would be adding to the larger number instead of finding out how far apart the numbers are.)

When is the count-up strategy useful?
(When the numbers are relatively close to each other.)

Day 1

Show a subtraction flash card, for example $9 - 6 = \square$.

Which number is greater?
(9)

Which number is less?
(6)

Continue this activity using subtraction flash cards with a difference of 1, 2, or 3.

Extension Present facts with minuends to 99 and a difference of 1, 2, or 3.

Which number is (greater or less)?

Day 2

Show two number cards, for example 8 and 6.

What subtraction sentence can be created using these two numbers?
($8 - 6 = 2$)

Continue this activity using number cards 3 through 12. Pair cards that have a difference of 1, 2, or 3.

Extension Use number cards 13 though 99.

Day 3

Present these facts.

6 − 5 (1)	8 − 6 (2)
4 − 4 (0)	10 − 9 (1)
5 − 3 (2)	8 − 8 (0)
3 − 2 (1)	4 − 2 (2)
7 − 7 (0)	5 − 4 (1)
9 − 8 (1)	3 − 3 (0)
6 − 4 (2)	0 − 0 (0)
3 − 1 (2)	2 − 1 (1)
2 − 2 (0)	10 − 8 (2)
4 − 3 (1)	7 − 5 (2)

Extension Present facts with minuends to 99 and a difference of 1, 2, or 3.

Day 5

Present these facts.

6 − 4 (2)	4 − 3 (1)
12 − 9 (3)	8 − 7 (1)
11 − 10 (1)	3 − 3 (0)
4 − 4 (0)	4 − 1 (3)
6 − 3 (3)	7 − 5 (2)
10 − 8 (2)	2 − 1 (1)
7 − 4 (3)	7 − 7 (0)
6 − 6 (0)	5 − 3 (2)
5 − 2 (3)	8 − 5 (3)
12 − 10 (2)	9 − 6 (3)

Extension Present facts with minuends to 99 and a difference of 1, 2, or 3.

Day 4

Present these facts.

7 − 4 (3)	4 − 1 (3)
6 − 6 (0)	9 − 9 (0)
1 − 0 (1)	7 − 5 (2)
9 − 7 (2)	7 − 6 (1)
5 − 2 (3)	8 − 5 (3)
9 − 6 (3)	1 − 1 (0)
5 − 5 (0)	8 − 6 (2)
11 − 9 (2)	3 − 0 (3)
10 − 7 (3)	3 − 2 (1)
9 − 8 (1)	11 − 8 (3)

Extension Present facts with minuends through 99 that have differences of 0, 1, 2, or 3.

Fact-Families Strategy Overview

What is the Fact-Families Strategy?

The fact-families strategy groups together four facts (in the case of doubles facts, two facts) that contain the same numbers. An example of a fact family is $4 + 2 = 6$, $2 + 4 = 6$, $6 - 4 = 2$, and $6 - 2 = 4$. This strategy helps children who know their addition facts extend their knowledge to subtraction.

Prerequisites

Children should understand subtraction concepts (pages vi-vii). They should know their addition facts.

When to Use the Fact-Families Strategy

The fact-families strategy can be used with all subtraction facts.

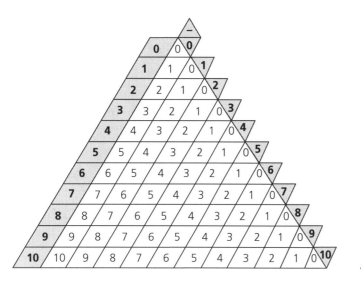

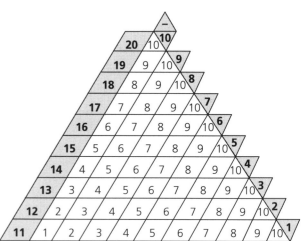

Additional Experiences

Have students use two different colors or shapes to make designs of up to twenty (20) elements. Children should write all four addition and subtraction facts that could be used to describe the design. Display the designs around the classroom.

Additional practice can be found in *Practice Your Facts, Levels 1–5*, by Creative Publications.

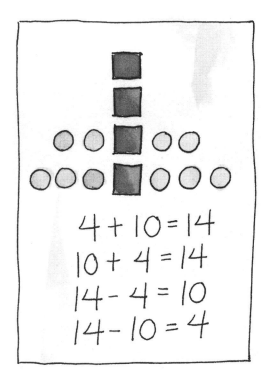

Fact-Families Strategy

Warm-ups

Each warm-up exercise set should take two (2) or three (3) minutes. The short exercise sets are great for filling transition times. Some teachers use them while children stand in line.

Materials

▶ Number cards 0 through 100

▶ Addition flash cards

▶ Subtraction flash cards

Talk About It

As the children work through these warm-ups, ask them to talk about their thinking. This not only helps you assess, but gives children a chance to clarify their thinking and to hear about ways of thinking that might be different from theirs. You might ask questions like

What is the relationship among the three numbers in a fact family?
(When one of the lesser numbers is subtracted from the greatest, the answer is the other lesser number. Or, the greatest number is the sum of the two lesser numbers.)

Which number will be the number that is being subtracted from?
(The greatest number will be the number being subtracted from.)

Which number will be the sum of the addition?
(The greatest number will be the sum.)

Day 1

Present children with three numbers, for example 3, 7, and 4.

What are two addition facts you can create using all three numbers?
(3 + 4 = 7 and 4 + 3 = 7)

What are two subtraction facts you can create using all three numbers?
(7 − 3 = 4 and 7 − 4 = 3)

Continue this activity using numbers 0 through 12. Group three numbers so that the greatest number is the sum of the other two.

Extension Use numbers through 100.

Day 2

Show children two number cards, for example 2 and 5.

What are two addition facts that you can create using these two numbers?
(2 + 5 = 7 and 5 + 2 = 7)

What are the two related subtraction facts for these numbers?
(7 − 5 = 2 and 7 − 2 = 5)

Continue this activity using numbers 0 through 10.

Extension Present a number 0 through 10 with a second number greater than ten.

Day 3

Show a subtraction flash card, for example
7 − 4 = □ .

What is the related subtraction fact?
(7 − 3 = 4)

What are the two related addition facts in this fact family?
(3 + 4 = 7 and 4 + 3 = 7)

Extension Present subtraction facts in which the minuend is larger than 10.

Day 4

Show an addition flash card, for example
4 + 5 = □ .

What are the two subtraction facts related to this addition fact?
(9 − 5 = 4 and 9 − 4 = 5)
Repeat this activity with several different addition facts. Children should be able to supply related facts with ease.

Extension Present children with addition sentences in which one addend is greater than 10.

Day 5

Show two number cards, for example 8 and 1.

What fact family can be made using these two numbers?
(Two different families can be made. 8 + 1 = 9, 1 + 8 = 9, 9 − 1 = 8, and 9 − 8 = 1 are the members of one fact family.
The second fact family is 8 − 1 = 7, 8 − 7 = 1, 1 + 7 = 8, and 7 + 1 = 8.)

Continue this activity using numbers 0 through 10.

Extension Present a number 0 through 10 with a second number greater than ten.

notes It would be a good idea to record responses for Day 5 on the board.

When the first fact is given, children may offer remaining members of that family and not think of facts from the second family. If that happens, after all four facts have been given ask children if they can think of another fact that can be made using the numbers.

On the other hand, if a child offers a fact from the second family before the first family is complete, write the fact, being sure to separate it from members of the first family. Children can then offer facts from either family.

Fact-Family Stories

Summary

Children write stories that include all the facts in one fact family.

Materials

For each child

▶ A copy of Fact-Family Stories, page 32

▶ A sheet of blank paper

▶ Ten (10) LinkerCubes®

Directions

❶ Read the story Frog Pond, page 32, along with your children. Have children use LinkerCubes® to "act out" the story on their papers as you read. Children should write the facts that are used in the story ($3 + 1 = 4$, $4 - 3 = 1$, $1 + 3 = 4$, $4 - 1 = 3$).

❷ Discuss fact families with your class. If fact families are a new idea for your children, spend time developing the concept by working with children to generate families for several facts.

❸ Invite children to write their own fact-family stories following the directions on page 32. Have children write one fact, then think of and write the three related facts in the spaces provided. You might want to assign fact families so that many different facts are covered. Completed stories can then be put together to make a class book.

notes

Hints for Writing Stories

Children should have the facts represent the characters in their story.

If writing about animals, children should make the characters all the same kind of animal.

Children should write the facts in order and have the number at the end of one fact be the first number of the next fact. They should then write their stories with the facts in that order. For example, $4 + 2 = 6$, $6 - 4 = 2$, $2 + 4 = 6$, $6 - 2 = 4$.

There are sixty-six (66) fact families. Here are some from which to choose:

0, 1, 1	2, 8, 10	4, 10, 14	6, 10, 16
1, 1, 2	2, 9, 11	5, 5, 10	7, 9, 16
1, 7, 8	3, 9, 12	5, 9, 14	7, 10, 17
1, 10, 11	3, 10, 13	5, 10, 15	9, 9, 18
2, 4, 6	4, 7, 11	6, 9, 15	9, 10, 19
10, 10, 20			

Extension or Homework Provide each child with one (1) copy of Fact-Family Search, page 33. Instruct children to draw a closed curve around each group of three members that make up a family.

Some solutions for Fact-Family Search are shown here.

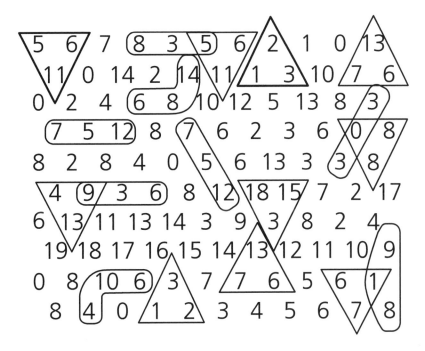

Fact-Family Stories

Frog Pond

Three frogs were sunning themselves on a log in the pond. Another frog joined them. Then there were four frogs on the log. A big bird flew overhead and three of the frogs jumped into the pond. One frog was still sitting on the log. The bird flew away and the three frogs climbed back onto the log. Once again there were four frogs on the log. Then one frog decided to go for a swim and jumped into the water. Three frogs were left on the log.

Write all the facts in the fact-family story above.

Directions

❶ Make up your own fact-family story. Write the facts you will use on the back of this page.

❷ On another piece of paper, draw a picture to show where your story takes place.

❸ Write your story below your picture.

❹ On the back of that paper, write the facts that are in your story.

Fact-Family Search

Draw a line around sets of three numbers that combine
to make up a fact. Think about the family of each fact you find.
Facts may overlap.

5   6   7   8   3   5   6   2   1   0   13

11   0   14   2   14   11   1   3   10   7   6

0   2   4   6   8   10   12   5   13   8   3

7   5   12   8   7   6   2   3   6   0   8

8   2   8   4   0   5   6   13   3   3   8

4   9   3   6   8   12   18   15   7   2   17

6   13   11   13   14   3   9   3   8   2   4

19   18   17   16   15   14   13   12   11   10   9

0   8   10   6   3   7   7   6   5   6   1

8   4   0   1   2   3   4   5   6   7   8

Fact-Family Strategy

Practice

Work on these sets of practice exercises until children can get each answer within three (3) seconds. Ask children to state the entire fact rather than just the answer. Stating the complete fact improves students' recall. Present the facts in various ways. Ask the children to listen and then reply verbally, or use flash cards and have the children write their facts. Varying the format helps all children focus on the facts.

Talk About It

Encourage children to talk about their thinking. Ask questions like

What is a fact family?

(A fact family is a set of four facts, two different addition facts and two different subtraction facts, that contain the same numbers. In the case of doubles facts, there are only two facts in the family.)

How are the three numbers in a fact family related?

(The sum of the two lesser numbers is the greatest number. When one of the two lesser numbers is subtracted from the greatest number, the other remains.)

How can we make an addition fact into a subtraction fact?

(Subtract one of the addends from the sum. The other addend is the difference.)

How can we make a subtraction fact into an addition fact?

(Add the difference and the subtrahend. The result is the minuend.)

Day 1

Present addition facts. After each, ask

What is the sum?
What is the related addition fact?
What are the two related subtraction facts?

6 + 4 (10)
(4 + 6 = 10; 10 − 6 = 4 and 10 − 4 = 6)

8 + 5 (13)
(5 + 8 = 13; 13 − 8 = 5 and 13 − 5 = 8)

2 + 7 (9)
(7 + 2 = 9; 9 − 2 = 7 and 9 − 7 = 2)

0 + 3 (3)
(3 + 0 = 3; 3 − 0 = 3 and 3 − 3 = 0)

5 + 5 (10)
(10 − 5 = 5)

Extension Present addition facts that have one addend greater than 12.

Day 2

Present these subtraction facts. After each, ask

What is the difference?

What is the other subtraction fact?

What are the two related addition facts?

12 − 5 (7)
(12 − 7 = 5; 5 + 7 = 12 and 7 + 5 = 12)

9 − 3 (6)
(9 − 6 = 3; 3 + 6 = 9 and 6 + 3 = 9)

11 − 8 (3)
(11 − 3 = 8; 8 + 3 = 11 and 3 + 8 = 11)

5 − 1 (4)
(5 − 4 = 1; 1 + 4 = 5 and 4 + 1 = 5)

8 − 0 (8)
(8 − 8 = 0; 0 + 8 = 8 and 8 + 0 = 8)

Extension Present subtraction facts that have minuends greater than 20.

Day 3

Show children an addition flash card, for example 3 + 8 = ☐ .

What is the sum?
(11)

What are the other three facts in this fact family?
(8 + 3 = 11, 11 − 8 = 3, and 11 − 3 = 8)

Continue using facts with addends of less than 10.

Extension Present addition facts that have one addend greater than 10.

Day 4

Show a subtraction flash card, for example 9 − 2 = ☐.

What is the difference?
(7)

What are the other three facts in this fact family?
(9 − 7 = 2, 2 + 7 = 9, and 7 + 2 = 9)

Continue using facts that have minuends of 20 or less.

Extension Present children with subtraction facts that have minuends greater than 20.

Day 5

Show both addition and subtraction flash cards.

What is the sum/difference?

What are the other three facts in the fact family?

Continue with addition facts that have addends of 10 or less and subtraction facts that have minuends of less than 20.

Extension Present addition facts that have one addend greater than 10 and subtraction facts that have minuends greater than 20.

Think-Addition Strategy Overview

What is the Think-Addition Strategy?

The think-addition strategy allows children to find a difference by knowing their addition facts. Children can, for example, rewrite the subtraction sentence 8 − 3 = □ as the addition sentence □ + 3 = 8. Since 5 + 3 = 8, the difference for the subtraction fact is 8.

The think-addition strategy is different from of the fact-family strategy. With the fact-family strategy, all of the numbers in one sentence must be known and three related sentences can be written. The think-addition strategy focuses on the relationship between addition and subtraction.

When to Use the Think-Addition Strategy

The think-addition strategy can be used with any subtraction fact.

Prerequisites

Children should understand subtraction concepts (pages vi-vii). They should know all their addition facts.

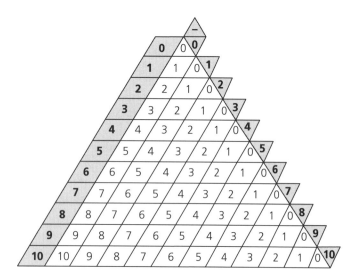

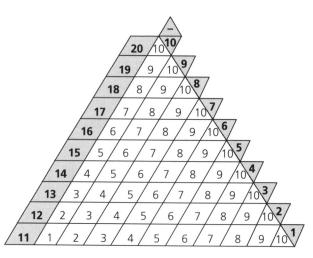

Additional Experiences

Write the numbers 2 through 20 on separate sheets of paper. Place LinkerCubes® of one color on each paper. The cubes placed on each sheet should be fewer in number than the numeral that is written on the paper.

Each child will need a sheet of paper for "fact collection." Children will collect as many facts as they can by writing addition sentences on their fact collection paper. Each fact will include the number written on a paper and the number of cubes placed there. For example, if the paper numbered 14 has 5 cubes, children write $5 + \square = 14$.

Using LinkerCubes of a different color, children place additional cubes on the paper to make the total number of cubes match the number written on the paper. They then fill in the missing addend on their fact collection paper.

Additional practice can be found in *Practice Your Facts, Levels 1–5,* by Creative Publications.

Think-Addition Strategy

Warm-ups

Each warm-up exercise set should take two (2) or three (3) minutes. The short exercise sets are great for filling transition times. Some teachers use them while children stand in line.

Materials

Number cards 0–100

Talk About It

As the children work through these warm-ups, ask them to talk about their thinking. This not only helps you assess, but gives children a chance to clarify their thinking and to hear about ways of thinking that might be different from theirs. You might ask questions like

How are the numbers in a subtraction fact related to addition?

(In subtraction, a number is separated into two parts. When the two parts are put back together by addition, they make the original number.)

How are the numbers in an addition fact related to subtraction?

(In addition, two numbers are put together to give a sum. If either of those numbers is subtracted from the sum, the other number will remain.)

A great question to keep the discussion going is

Does anyone have a different way of thinking about this question?

Day 1

Show two number cards, for example 6 and 8.

Which number is less?

(6)

How many less?

(2)

Continue using number cards 0 through 12. Pair cards that have a difference of 1 or 2.

Extension Present number cards through 100 in pairs that have a difference of 1 or 2.

Day 2

Show two number cards, for example 8 and 11.

Which number is less?
(8)

How many less?
(3)

Continue using number cards 0 through 12. Pair cards that have a difference of 4 or less.

Extension Present numbers cards through 100 in pairs that have a difference of 4 or less.

Day 3

Show number cards, for example 9 and 3.

Which number is less?
(3)

How many less?
(6)

Continue using number cards 0 through 12. Pair cards that have a difference of 6 or less.

Extension Present numbers cards through 100 in pairs that have a difference of 6 or less.

Day 4

Show two number cards, for example 12 and 7.

Which number is less?
(7)

How many less?
(5)

Continue using number cards 0 through 12. Pair cards that have a difference of 6 or less.

Extension Present number cards through 100 in pairs that have a difference of 6 or less.

....

Day 5

Present missing addend questions.

5 plus what number equals 7?

(2)

What is 7 − 2?

(5)

Continue with questions that call for missing addends of 2 or less. Limit sums to 20.

Extension Use sums greater than 20.

....

Day 6

Present missing addend questions.

4 plus what number equals 8?

(4)

What is 8 − 4?

(4)

Continue with questions that call for missing addends of 4 or less. Limit sums to 20.

Extension Use sums greater than 20.

....

Day 7

Present missing addend questions.

5 plus what number equals 11?

(6)

What is 11 − 5?

(6)

Continue with questions that call for missing addends of 6 or less. Limit sums to 20.

Extension Use sums greater than 20.

Day 8

Present missing addend questions.

7 plus what number equals 15?
(8)

Continue with questions that call for missing addends of 0 to 8. Limit sums to 20.

Extension Use sums greater than 20.

Day 9

Present missing addend questions.

2 plus what number equals 11?
(9)

Continue with questions that call for missing addends of 0 to 9. Limit sums to 20.

Extension Use sums greater than 20.

Day 10

Present missing addend questions.

7 plus what number equals 16?
(9)

Continue with questions that call for missing addends of 0 to 10. Limit sums to 20.

Extension Use sums greater than 20.

Opposite Faces

Summary

Children roll specially prepared number cubes, then write addition and subtraction facts for the numbers rolled.

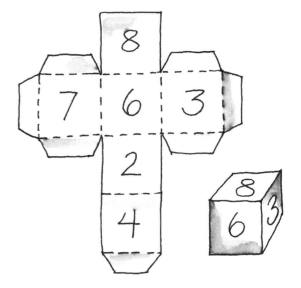

●●●

Small Group Activity

Materials

Each pair needs

▶ A copy of Opposite Faces, page 44

▶ Three (3) special number cubes (see note)

Directions

❶ Explain that numbers on opposite faces of a number cube are to be added together. The sum of opposite sides is different for each cube, but on a given cube opposite sides will have the same sum. Children should verify this by adding opposite faces of their cubes.

❷ Provide an example for your children by working through one exercise on page 44 with them. Allow children to choose which number cube to use for each exercise.

note Three number cubes, a "10 cube," a "12 cube," and a "13 cube" are needed for this activity. The "10 cube" has opposite faces with sums of 10 (6, 4; 7, 3; 8, 2). The "12 cube" has opposite faces with sums of 12 (7, 5; 8, 4; and 9, 3). The "13 cube" has opposite faces with sums of 13 (6, 7; 8, 5; 9, 4). Numbers can be written on blank number cubes or cubes can be made by folding and taping cube nets.

Talk About It

Ask children questions like

Were you able to figure out the number on the opposite side of the number cube without looking? How?

(Accept all reasonable answers. Record methods on the board.)

When a child answers with the think-addition strategy, record the response as an addition fact with a box for the missing addend. Then ask

How can this way of thinking help you to find the answer for 15 − 8?

($8 + \Box = 15$, $8 + 7 = 15$, so $15 − 8 = 7$) Repeat this line of questioning using several different facts.

Extension or Homework

Extend practice with this strategy by having children complete Opposite Sides, page 45.

Name _____

Opposite Sides

You will be given the sum for opposite faces on a number cube. When you know the number on one face, can you figure out what number is on the face opposite it without looking? Try it. Then use the numbers to write a subtraction sentence.

1. Sum = 14   [8] + ___ = 14   ___ − ___ = ___
2. Sum = 15   [7] + ___ = ___   ___ − ___ = ___
3. Sum = 15   [6] + ___ = ___   ___ − ___ = ___
4. Sum = 13   [8] + ___ = ___   ___ − ___ = ___
5. Sum = 12   [3] + ___ = ___   ___ − ___ = ___
6. Sum = 12   [5] + ___ = ___   ___ − ___ = ___
7. Sum = 11   [4] + ___ = ___   ___ − ___ = ___
8. Sum = 11   [6] + ___ = ___   ___ − ___ = ___
9. Sum = 12   [8] + ___ = ___   ___ − ___ = ___
10. Sum = 10 [7] + ___ = ___   ___ − ___ = ___

SUBTRACTION | Facts That Last 45

Opposite Faces

Try to tell the hidden number of the number cube without looking.

Materials

A "10 cube," a "12 cube," and a "13 cube"

Directions

1 Select one cube to use.

2 Fill in the blank after "Sum = " to tell which cube you are using.

3 Roll the cube. Write the number that lands on top of the cube in the box on your paper.

4 Write the addition fact that has your sum and the number you rolled as one addend. Complete the fact by writing the missing addend where it belongs in the fact. Draw a ring around that addend.

5 Write the related subtraction sentence.

1. Sum = ___ [ ] + ___ ≈ _____   _____ − ___ ≈ _____

2. Sum = ___ [ ] + ___ ≈ _____   _____ − ___ ≈ _____

3. Sum = ___ [ ] + ___ ≈ _____   _____ − ___ ≈ _____

4. Sum = ___ [ ] + ___ ≈ _____   _____ − ___ ≈ _____

5. Sum = ___ [ ] + ___ ≈ _____   _____ − ___ ≈ _____

6. Sum = ___ [ ] + ___ ≈ _____   _____ − ___ ≈ _____

© Creative Publications 32311

Opposite Sides

You will be given the sum for opposite faces on a number cube. When you know the number on one face, can you figure out what number is on the face opposite it without looking? Try it. Then use the numbers to write a subtraction sentence.

1. Sum = 14   8 + ___ = 14 ___ − ___ = _____

2. Sum = 15   7 + ___ = _____   ___ − ___ = _____

3. Sum = 15   6 + ___ = _____   ___ − ___ = _____

4. Sum = 13   8 + ___ = _____   ___ − ___ = _____

5. Sum = 12   3 + ___ = _____   ___ − ___ = _____

6. Sum = 12   5 + ___ = _____   ___ − ___ = _____

7. Sum = 11   4 + ___ = _____   ___ − ___ = _____

8. Sum = 11   6 + ___ = _____   ___ − ___ = _____

9. Sum = 12   8 + ___ = _____   ___ − ___ = _____

10. Sum = 10   7 + ___ = _____   ___ − ___ = _____

Think-Addition Strategy

Practice

Work on these sets of practice exercises until children can get each answer within three (3) seconds. Ask children to state the entire fact rather than just the answer. Stating the complete fact improves students' recall. Present the facts in various ways. Ask the children to listen and then reply verbally, or use flash cards and have the children write their facts. Varying the format helps all children focus on the facts.

Talk About It

Encourage children to talk about their thinking. Follow up by asking if anyone has a different way to find an answer.

Which number in a subtraction fact would be an addend in an addition fact?

(The number being subtracted would be an addend.)

Which number in a subtraction fact would be the sum for an addition fact?

(The number from which an amount is being subtracted would be the sum for an addition fact.)

How do fact families help you to think of addition facts?

(When you have a subtraction fact, understanding about fact families can help to think of two related addition facts.)

Day 1

Present these facts.

6 − 5 (1)	9 − 7 (2)
3 − 1 (2)	7 − 6 (1)
4 − 4 (0)	5 − 5 (0)
8 − 7 (1)	2 − 1 (1)
6 − 4 (2)	4 − 2 (2)
3 − 2 (1)	8 − 8 (0)
9 − 9 (0)	1 − 0 (1)
7 − 5 (2)	5 − 3 (2)
2 − 2 (0)	8 − 6 (2)
4 − 3 (1)	3 − 3 (0)

Extension Present facts using numbers through 99. Select numbers that have a difference of 0, 1, or 2.

Day 2

Present these facts.

9 − 5 (4)	6 − 6 (0)
7 − 4 (3)	10 − 6 (4)
5 − 4 (1)	11 − 8 (3)
6 − 2 (4)	10 − 9 (1)
7 − 7 (0)	1 − 1 (0)
9 − 6 (3)	11 − 7 (4)
10 − 8 (2)	6 − 4 (2)
4 − 0 (4)	8 − 5 (3)
5 − 2 (3)	11 − 9 (2)
2 − 0 (2)	6 − 3 (3)

Extension Present facts using numbers through 99. Select numbers that have differences of 0 to 4.

Day 3

Present these facts.

9 − 3 (6)	6 − 1 (5)
11 − 6 (5)	9 − 7 (2)
8 − 4 (4)	10 − 4 (6)
7 − 1 (6)	12 − 7 (5)
12 − 8 (4)	7 − 3 (4)
9 − 4 (5)	8 − 6 (2)
6 − 5 (1)	4 − 3 (1)
10 − 7 (3)	10 − 5 (5)
12 − 6 (6)	8 − 3 (5)
8 − 2 (6)	11 − 5 (6)

Extension Present facts using numbers through 99. Select numbers that have differences of 0 to 6.

Day 4

Present these facts.

9 − 2 (7)	11 − 2 (9)
11 − 3 (8)	12 − 4 (8)
13 − 4 (9)	16 − 9 (7)
10 − 2 (8)	14 − 7 (7)
8 − 1 (7)	12 − 3 (9)
13 − 6 (7)	9 − 3 (6)
14 − 9 (5)	10 − 6 (4)
11 − 7 (4)	13 − 7 (6)
8 − 3 (5)	15 − 7 (8)
15 − 6 (9)	13 − 5 (8)

Extension Present facts using numbers through 99. Select numbers that have differences of 0 to 10.

Day 5

Present these facts.

8 − 6 (2)	4 − 4 (0)
5 − 4 (1)	8 − 7 (1)
8 − 8 (0)	3 − 2 (1)
7 − 5 (2)	10 − 8 (2)
10 − 9 (1)	6 − 6 (0)
3 − 1 (2)	4 − 3 (1)
5 − 5 (0)	11 − 9 (2)
1 − 0 (1)	9 − 8 (1)
4 − 2 (2)	2 − 2 (0)
9 − 7 (2)	7 − 6 (1)

Extension Present facts using greater numbers with a difference of 0, 1, or 2.

Day 6

Present these facts.

7 − 3 (4)	7 − 4 (3)
9 − 6 (3)	5 − 3 (2)
11 − 7 (4)	8 − 4 (4)
12 − 9 (3)	10 − 7 (3)
2 − 1 (1)	9 − 8 (1)
8 − 5 (3)	8 − 6 (2)
10 − 6 (4)	9 − 5 (4)
9 − 7 (2)	11 − 8 (3)
3 − 3 (0)	7 − 5 (2)
12 − 8 (4)	9 − 9 (0)

Extension Present facts using numbers through 99. Select numbers that have differences of 0 to 4.

Day 7

Present these facts.

13 − 7 (6)	11 − 5 (6)
11 − 6 (5)	12 − 7 (5)
9 − 5 (4)	13 − 8 (5)
14 − 8 (6)	12 − 6 (6)
12 − 9 (3)	11 − 7 (4)
10 − 6 (4)	9 − 6 (3)
9 − 4 (5)	10 − 4 (6)
15 − 9 (6)	14 − 9 (5)
7 − 4 (3)	13 − 9 (4)
12 − 8 (4)	10 − 5 (5)

Extension Present facts using numbers through 99. Select numbers that have differences of 0 to 6.

Day 8

Present these facts.

15 − 7 (8)	12 − 5 (7)
13 − 6 (7)	14 − 8 (6)
12 − 7 (5)	16 − 9 (7)
11 − 5 (6)	13 − 5 (8)
14 − 6 (8)	14 − 9 (5)
11 − 4 (7)	12 − 4 (8)
17 − 9 (8)	15 − 8 (7)
13 − 8 (5)	13 − 7 (6)
12 − 6 (6)	14 − 7 (7)
16 − 8 (8)	9 − 4 (5)

Extension Present facts using numbers through 99. Select numbers that have differences of 0 to 9.

Day 9

Present these facts.

16 − 7 (9)	11 − 3 (8)
14 − 6 (8)	14 − 9 (5)
13 − 4 (9)	13 − 7 (6)
12 − 5 (7)	14 − 5 (9)
15 − 7 (8)	16 − 8 (8)
15 − 9 (6)	11 − 4 (7)
18 − 9 (9)	12 − 3 (9)
12 − 4 (8)	13 − 5 (8)
13 − 6 (7)	15 − 6 (9)
17 − 8 (9)	15 − 8 (7)

Extension Present facts using numbers through 99. Select numbers that have differences of 0 to 9.

Day 10

Present these facts.

14 − 5 (9)	16 − 8 (8)
17 − 9 (8)	11 − 4 (7)
10 − 7 (3)	12 − 8 (4)
16 − 7 (9)	11 − 6 (5)
15 − 8 (7)	13 − 4 (9)
13 − 5 (8)	15 − 7 (8)
12 − 7 (5)	17 − 8 (9)
13 − 9 (4)	14 − 6 (8)
15 − 6 (9)	18 − 9 (9)
8 − 6 (2)	8 − 5 (3)

Extension Present facts using numbers through 99. Select numbers that have differences of 0 to 9.

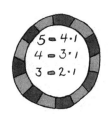

Patterns Strategy Overview

What is the Patterns Strategy?

Many subtraction facts follow patterns that make them easier to remember. The patterns strategy focuses attention on those patterns. The patterns most easily observed are those formed when subtracting 0, 1, 9, 10; subtracting the number from itself; or subtracting one less than the number.

When to Use the Patterns Strategy

The patterns strategy can be used when subtracting 0, 1, 9, or 10; when subtracting a number equal to the minuend; and when subtracting a number equal to one less than the minuend.

Prerequisites

Children should understand subtraction concepts (pages vi-vii). They should be able to identify and describe patterns.

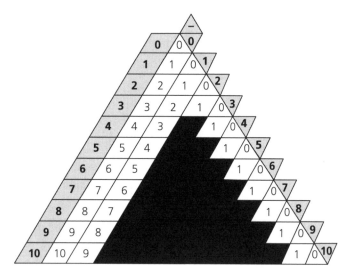

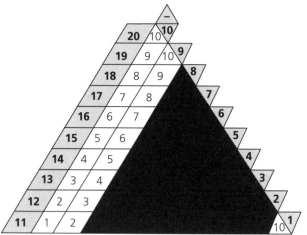

Additional Experiences

Provide each child with a blank subtraction chart, page 85. Direct children to fill in their charts and then look for patterns in the completed charts. Hold a class discussion about the patterns found.

Additional practice can be found in *Practice Your Facts, Levels 1–5,* by Creative Publications.

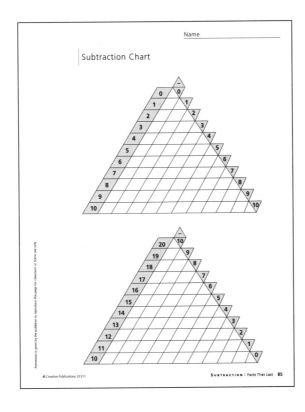

Name

Subtraction Chart

© Creative Publications 32311

SUBTRACTION | Facts That Last **85**

Patterns Strategy

Warm-ups

Each warm-up exercise set should take two (2) or three (3) minutes. The short exercise sets are great for filling transition times. Some teachers use them while children stand in line.

Materials

Number cards 0–100

Talk About It

As the children work through these warm-ups, ask them to talk about their thinking. This not only helps you assess, but gives children a chance to clarify their thinking and to hear about ways of thinking that might be different from theirs. You might ask questions like

When is the difference of a subtraction fact 0?
(Any number minus itself is zero.)

When is the difference of a subtraction fact 1?
(Any number minus a number one less than itself equals one.)

How do you find the difference when 10 is subtracted from a number?
(When subtracting ten, the tens digit is decreased by one.)

....

Day 1

Show children a number, for example 7.

What is this number?
(7)

What number comes before (the number)?
(6)

Continue this activity using number cards 0 through 12.

Extension Repeat activity presenting numbers greater than 12.

....

Day 2

Show children a number card, for example 96.

Count back. Start with this number and count by 10.
(96, 86, 76, 66, 56, 46, 36, 26, 16, 6.)

Use number cards from 91 through 100. Use each card at least one time.

Extension Show number cards 11 through 100. Have children count back by tens from each card shown.

Day 3
Show children a number card, for example 16.

Count back 10.
(6)

Count on 1 from the new number.
(7)

How much has been subtracted from the number on the card?
(9)

Continue with number cards 11 through 20 using each card at least once.

Extension Use number cards from 21 through 100.

Day 4
Show children a number card, for example 8.

What number would you subtract to have a difference of 0?
(8)

Continue with number cards 1 through 10 using each card at least once.

Extension Use numbers greater than 10.

Day 5
Show children a number card, for example 2.

What number would you subtract to have a difference of 1?
(1)

Continue with number cards 0 through 10 using each card at least once.

Extension Use numbers greater than 10.

Subtraction Patterns

Summary

Children examine lists of subtraction facts and look for patterns. As children identify and describe the patterns they find, the facts become easier to remember.

Individual Activity

Materials

A copy of Subtraction Patterns, page 56, for each child

Directions

❶ Have children examine the groups of facts on page 56 to find as many patterns as possible.

❷ Encourage children to write notes describing patterns found and to be prepared to tell about those patterns during class discussion.

notes Many different patterns can be found for these sets of facts. Here is a sampling:

Set A
Subtracting 0—any number minus zero equals itself.

Set B
Subtracting 1—any number minus one is the counting number that comes before that number.

Set C
Subtracting the number from itself—any number minus itself equals zero.

Set D
Subtracting an amount one less than the number itself—any number minus a number one less than itself equals one.

Set E
Subtracting 10—when subtracting ten, the tens digit is made smaller by one. *Also,* a number with one in its tens place minus ten equals the number in the ones place.

Set F
Subtracting 9—any number minus nine equals one more than that same number minus ten. *Also,* when subtracting nine from a number with one in its tens place, just add the two digits of the minuend. For example, $16 - 9$ is $1 + 6$ or 7. $16 - 9 = 7$.

Talk About It

For each set of subtraction facts, ask questions like

What patterns did you find for this set of subtraction facts?

(See the notes for selected patterns for each set. Accept all reasonable observations.)

Can you use the patterns you found to make a rule that will make it easy to remember the facts?

(Guide children in turning responses into general rules that are as clear and concise as possible.)

Extension or Homework   Provide a copy of Color Coded, page 57, for each child. Instruct children to use the rules they found to complete the page.

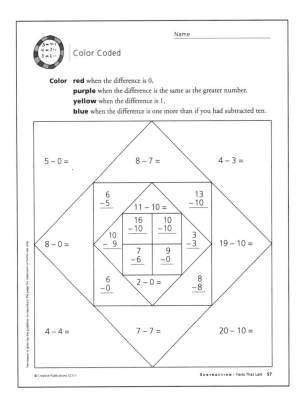

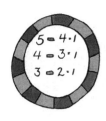

Subtraction Patterns

Look for patterns in each set of subtraction facts. Write notes about the patterns you find so you can share information with the class.

Set A

10 − 0 = 10	4 − 0 = 4
9 − 0 = 9	3 − 0 = 3
8 − 0 = 8	2 − 0 = 2
7 − 0 = 7	1 − 0 = 0
6 − 0 = 6	0 − 0 = 0
5 − 0 = 5	

Set B

10 − 1 = 9	5 − 1 = 4
9 − 1 = 8	4 − 1 = 3
8 − 1 = 7	3 − 1 = 2
7 − 1 = 6	2 − 1 = 1
6 − 1 = 5	1 − 1 = 0

Set C

10 − 10 = 0	4 − 4 = 0
9 − 9 = 0	3 − 3 = 0
8 − 8 = 0	2 − 2 = 0
7 − 7 = 0	1 − 1 = 0
6 − 6 = 0	0 − 0 = 0
5 − 5 = 0	

Set D

10 − 9 = 1	5 − 4 = 1
9 − 8 = 1	4 − 3 = 1
8 − 7 = 1	3 − 2 = 1
7 − 6 = 1	2 − 1 = 1
6 − 5 = 1	1 − 0 = 1

Set E

20 − 10 = 10	14 − 10 = 4
19 − 10 = 9	13 − 10 = 3
18 − 10 = 8	12 − 10 = 2
17 − 10 = 7	11 − 10 = 1
16 − 10 = 6	10 − 10 = 0
15 − 10 = 5	

Set F

18 − 9 = 9	13 − 9 = 4
17 − 9 = 8	12 − 9 = 3
16 − 9 = 7	11 − 9 = 2
15 − 9 = 6	10 − 9 = 1
14 − 9 = 5	

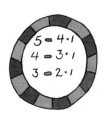

Color Coded

Color **red** when the difference is 0,

purple when the difference is the same as the greater number,

yellow when the difference is 1,

blue when the difference is one more than if you had subtracted ten.

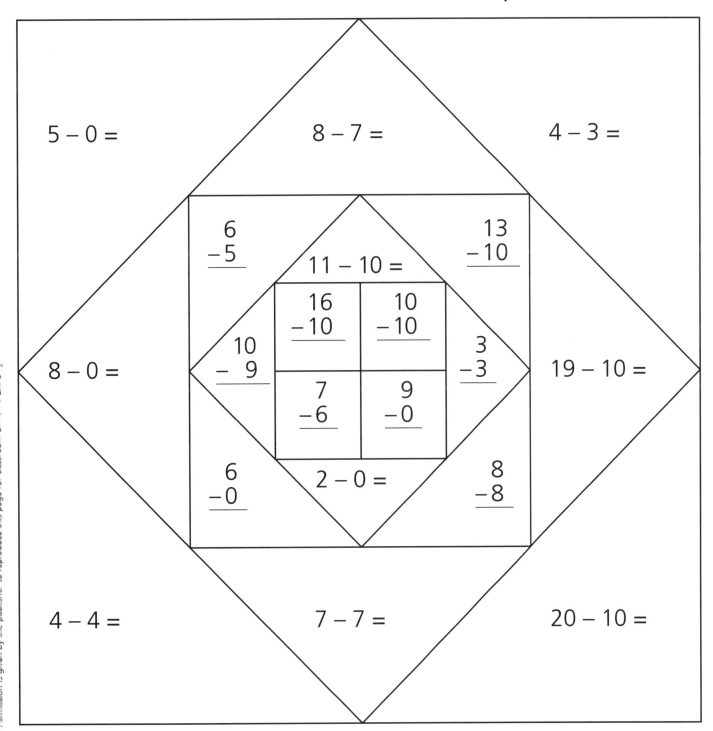

$5 - 0 =$

$8 - 7 =$

$4 - 3 =$

$8 - 0 =$

$19 - 10 =$

$4 - 4 =$

$7 - 7 =$

$20 - 10 =$

$$\begin{array}{r} 6 \\ -5 \\ \hline \end{array}$$

$$\begin{array}{r} 13 \\ -10 \\ \hline \end{array}$$

$11 - 10 =$

$$\begin{array}{r} 16 \\ -10 \\ \hline \end{array}$$

$$\begin{array}{r} 10 \\ -10 \\ \hline \end{array}$$

$$\begin{array}{r} 10 \\ -\ 9 \\ \hline \end{array}$$

$$\begin{array}{r} 3 \\ -3 \\ \hline \end{array}$$

$$\begin{array}{r} 7 \\ -6 \\ \hline \end{array}$$

$$\begin{array}{r} 9 \\ -0 \\ \hline \end{array}$$

$$\begin{array}{r} 6 \\ -0 \\ \hline \end{array}$$

$2 - 0 =$

$$\begin{array}{r} 8 \\ -8 \\ \hline \end{array}$$

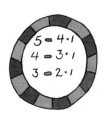

Patterns Strategy

Practice

Work on these sets of practice exercises until children can get each answer within three (3) seconds. Ask children to state the entire fact rather than just the answer. Stating the complete fact improves students' recall. Present the facts in various ways. Ask the children to listen and then reply verbally, or use flash cards and have the children write their facts. Varying the format helps all children focus on the facts.

Talk About It

Encourage children to talk about their thinking. Follow up by asking if anyone has a different way to find an answer.

What is the difference when 0 is subtracted from a number?

(Any number minus zero equals itself.)

What is the difference when 1 is subtracted from a number?

(Any number minus one yields the counting number that comes before the number.)

What is the pattern for subtracting 9?

(Any number minus nine equals one more than that same number minus ten.)

Day 1

Present these facts.

7 − 0 (7)	9 − 1 (8)
3 − 1 (2)	0 − 0 (0)
4 − 0 (4)	6 − 0 (6)
9 − 0 (9)	2 − 1 (1)
5 − 1 (4)	8 − 0 (8)
8 − 1 (7)	1 − 1 (0)
2 − 0 (2)	10 − 1 (9)
6 − 1 (5)	3 − 0 (3)
4 − 1 (3)	1 − 0 (1)
5 − 0 (5)	7 − 1 (6)

Extension Present facts in which 0 or 1 is subtracted from numbers greater than 10.

Day 2

Present these facts.

13 − 10 (3)	20 − 10 (10)
17 − 10 (7)	19 − 10 (9)
12 − 10 (2)	11 − 10 (1)
15 − 10 (5)	18 − 10 (8)
14 − 10 (4)	10 − 10 (0)
16 − 10 (6)	

Extension Present facts in which 10 is subtracted from numbers greater than 20.

Day 3

Present these facts.

12 − 9 (3)	17 − 9 (8)
15 − 9 (6)	10 − 9 (1)
19 − 9 (10)	13 − 9 (4)
11 − 9 (2)	16 − 9 (7)
18 − 9 (9)	20 − 9 (11)
14 − 9 (5)	

Extension Present facts in which 9 is subtracted from numbers greater than 20.

Day 4

Present these facts.

4 − 4 (0)	1 − 1 (0)
8 − 8 (0)	9 − 9 (0)
3 − 3 (0)	0 − 0 (0)
7 − 7 (0)	5 − 5 (0)
2 − 2 (0)	10 − 10 (0)
6 − 6 (0)	

Extension Present facts in which a number greater than 10 is subtracted from itself.

Day 5

Present these facts.

6 − 5 (1)	9 − 8 (1)
3 − 2 (1)	2 − 1 (1)
8 − 7 (1)	11 − 10 (1)
1 − 0 (1)	5 − 4 (1)
7 − 6 (1)	10 − 9 (1)
4 − 3 (1)	

Extension Present facts having numbers greater than 11 which result in a difference of 1.

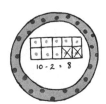

Subtract-from-Ten Strategy Overview

What is the Subtract-from-Ten Strategy?

The subtract-from-ten strategy focuses on a small but very important group of facts that have ten (10) as the minuend. Children can think of these facts by visualizing ten fingers or a ten-frame.

When to Use the Subtract-from-Ten Strategy

Use the subtract-from-ten strategy when the minuend is ten.

Prerequisites

Children should understand subtraction concepts (pages vi-vii). They should also know addition facts that have sums of ten.

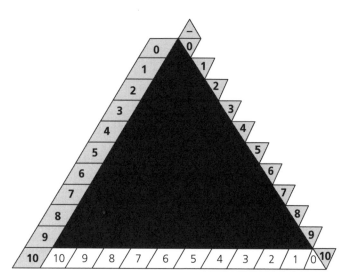

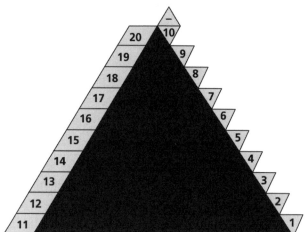

Additional Experiences

Each child will need paper and pencil. Call on children to model the story with bear counters or LinkerCubes® as you tell about a family of ten bears having a picnic. You might want to use a piece of green paper to represent grass and a blue circle to represent a wading pool. Start the story by saying:

Ten bears are having a picnic. They are all on the grass.

Have a child put all ten counters on the green area of the paper.

None of the bears are in the wading pool.

Write *10 − 0 = 10* on the board and ask children to write the equation on their papers.

The baby bear decided it was too warm on the grass and went to the wading pool to cool off.

Ask a child to move one counter to the wading pool.

Have children help you write 10 − 1 = 9 to represent the number of bears still on the grass. Continue moving bears one by one from the grass into the wading pool and writing facts until all the bears are in the wading pool.

Additional practice can be found in *Practice Your Facts, Levels 1–5*, by Creative Publications.

Subtract-from-Ten Strategy

Warm-ups

Each warm-up exercise set should take two (2) or three (3) minutes. The short exercise sets are great for filling transition times. Some teachers use them while children stand in line.

Materials

Number cards 0–10

Talk About It

As the children work through these warm-ups, ask them to talk about their thinking. This not only helps you assess, but gives children a chance to clarify their thinking and to hear about ways of thinking that might be different from theirs. You might ask questions like

How might other subtraction strategies be used to help you remember these facts?
(The count-back strategy can be used to subtract 1, 2, or 3 from 10; The count-up strategy for subtracting 9, 8, 7, and 6; and the fact-families strategy can be used with any fact.)

A great question to keep the discussion going is

Did anyone think of a different strategy to remember these facts?

....
Day 1

Show a number card, for example 1.

Hold up 10 fingers. Take away this number of fingers.

How many fingers are left?
(9)

Continue with number cards 0 through 10. Show each card at least once.

Extension Have children work in pairs. Show number cards 0 through 20 and have children take away this number of fingers.

How many fingers are left?

....
Day 2

Show a number card, for example 3.

How many more to make 10?
(7)

Continue with number cards 0 through 10. Show each card at least once.

Extension Show number cards 11 through 20.

How many more to make 20?

Day 3

Show a number card, for example 4.

How many more to make 10?
(6)

Continue with number cards 0 through 10. Show each card at least once.

Extension Show number cards 11 through 20.

How many more to make 20?

Day 4

Show a number card, for example 8.

Subtract this number from 10.

What is the difference?
(2)

Continue with number cards 0 through 10. Show each card at least once.

Extension Show number cards 0 through 10.

Subtract this number from 20. What is the difference?

Day 5

Show children a number, say 5.

Subtract this number from 10.

What is the difference?
(5)

Continue with number cards 0 through 10. Show each card at least once.

Extension Show number cards from 0 through 10. Have children subtract the number from a multiple of 10.

Mental Images

Summary

Children use ten-frames to develop mental images of subtracting from ten.

Small Group Activity

Materials

Each pair needs

▶ A copy of Ten-Frame Subtraction, page 66

▶ Ten (10) LinkerCubes®

Directions

❶ Demonstrate how to represent each number from zero to ten in a ten-frame by filling the top row first from left to right, then the bottom row from left to right.

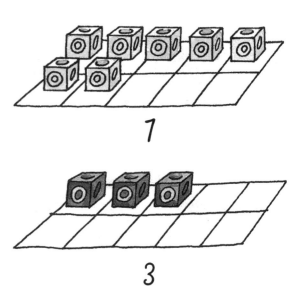

❷ Have children follow the instructions for Ten-Frame Subtraction, page 66, and find all eleven subtraction facts that begin with "10 − ."

Extension

Working in groups of four, children toss ten (10) two-color bean counters (or pennies) and generate subtraction facts with minuends of ten to complete Bean Toss, page 67. The result of each toss is recorded on a tally sheet.

When students have completed the activity, discuss findings with the class.

What is one fact you got when you tossed the beans?
Write the fact on the board.

Did anyone get a different fact?
Continue to write facts beginning with "10 –" on the board until you have all eleven facts.

Then ask
Are these eleven facts all the facts you can possibly get?
(Yes.)

How do you know?
(Accept all reasonable explanations.)

note It might be interesting to make a class tally. After all groups have contributed their information, have the children compare the number of tally marks next to each sum to determine which differences occur most frequently. Children could then compare the class frequencies with their group's results. (There might be a small variation or a large one, all dependent on chance.)

Why are the results for each group different?
(Because the beans land differently for each group.)

Which group is right?
(All of the groups are right. The tallies represent the chance landing of the beans.)

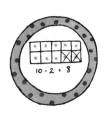

Ten-Frame Subtraction

Use a ten-frame and LinkerCubes® to find all the subtraction facts that begin with "10 – ."

Materials

▶ Ten (10) LinkerCubes®

▶ Paper and pencil

Directions

1 Place 10 cubes in the ten-frame.

2 Remove some of the cubes from the ten-frame.

3 On a separate piece of paper, write a subtraction fact that describes the difference between the full ten-frame and the number of cubes you removed.

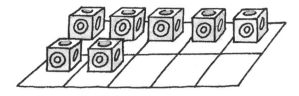

$10 - 3 = 7$

4 Repeat this activity until you have found all the possible facts starting with "10 – ."

5 Did you find all of the subtraction facts? Turn this paper over and explain how you know on the back.

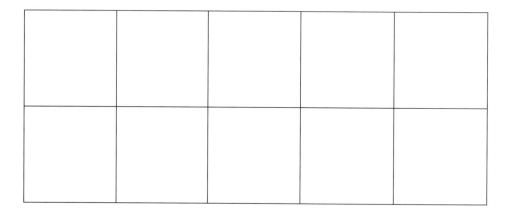

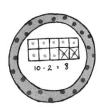

Bean Toss

How many different subtraction facts can you make by tossing ten (10) two-color beans?

Materials

Ten (10) two-color beans

Directions

1 Toss 10 two-color beans so they land on a desk. Count the number of beans that land white-side-up.

2 On a separate piece of paper, write a subtraction fact to describe the difference between the total number of beans and the number of white beans.

3 Make a tally mark in the chart next to the number that matches the difference.

4 Repeat this activity until you've tossed the beans 30 times.

10 − White Beans = Difference

Difference	Tally
10	
9	
8	
7	
6	
5	
4	
3	
2	
1	
0	

Subtract-from-Ten Strategy

Practice

Work on these sets of practice exercises until children can get each answer within three (3) seconds. Ask children to say or write the entire fact rather than just the answer. Present the facts in various ways. Have children listen and then reply verbally, or use flash cards and have the children write their facts. Varying the format helps all children focus on the facts.

Talk About It

Encourage children to talk about their thinking. Follow up by asking if anyone has a different way to find an answer.

What are some of the other subtraction strategies that you are using to help you remember these subtraction facts?
(The count-back, count-up, think-addition, and fact-families strategies can all be helpful.)

Why might the subtract-from-ten strategy be important to know?
(The subtract-from-ten strategy can be applied with any multiple of ten.)

Day 1

Present these facts.

10 − 7 (3)
10 − 2 (8)
10 − 5 (5)
10 − 6 (4)
10 − 9 (1)
10 − 3 (7)
10 − 8 (2)
10 − 0 (10)
10 − 1 (9)
10 − 4 (6)
10 − 10 (0)

Extension Present facts in which the numbers 0 through 10 are subtracted from 20.

Day 2

Present these facts.

10 − 8 (2)
10 − 4 (6)
10 − 0 (10)
10 − 3 (7)
10 − 6 (4)
10 − 9 (1)
10 − 5 (5)
10 − 2 (8)
10 − 10 (0)
10 − 1 (9)
10 − 7 (3)

Extension Present facts in which numbers 0 through 10 are subtracted from multiples of 10, with limit of 40.

Day 3

Present these facts.

10 − 9 (1)

10 − 2 (7)

10 − 10 (0)

10 − 4 (6)

10 − 3 (7)

10 − 0 (10)

10 − 7 (3)

10 − 1 (9)

10 − 5 (5)

10 − 8 (2)

10 − 6 (4)

Extension Present facts in which numbers 0 through 10 are subtracted from multiples of 10, with limit of 60.

Day 4

Present these facts.

10 − 6 (4)

10 − 3 (7)

10 − 5 (5)

10 − 9 (1)

10 − 0 (10)

10 − 8 (2)

10 − 4 (6)

10 − 10 (0)

10 − 1 (9)

10 − 7 (3)

10 − 2 (8)

Extension Present facts in which numbers 0 through 10 are subtracted from multiples of 10, with limit of 80.

Day 5

Present these facts.

10 − 7 (3)

10 − 1 (9)

10 − 4 (6)

10 − 2 (8)

10 − 0 (10)

10 − 5 (5)

10 − 9 (1)

10 − 6 (4)

10 − 3 (7)

10 − 10 (0)

10 − 8 (2)

Extension Present facts in which numbers 0 through 10 are subtracted from multiples of 10, with limit of 100.

Ten-Between Strategy Overview

What is the Ten-Between Strategy?

The ten-between strategy applies to facts that have a minuend greater than ten and a subtrahend of less than ten. The difference between ten and each number in the fact is found and the differences are added together. For example, with 12 − 8, 12 is 2 from 10 and 8 is 2 from 10. 2 + 2 = 4. So, 12 − 8 = 4.

Prerequisites

Children should understand subtraction concepts (pages vi-vii). They should also be adept at finding the difference between any number and ten.

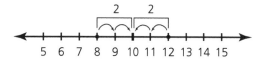

$$12 - 8 = 2 + 2 = 4$$

When to Use the Ten-Between Strategy

The ten-between strategy is best used when neither minuend nor subtrahend is far from ten.

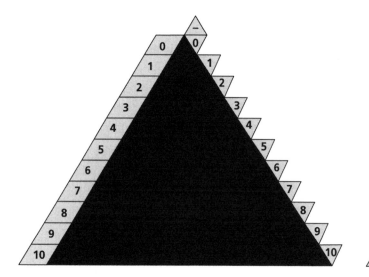

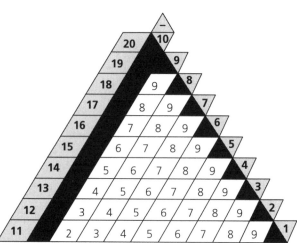

Additional Experiences

Demonstrate "ten-between" thinking with two
(2) ten-frames. Begin by drawing circles in
the ten-frames to represent a minuend greater
than ten. Identify the subtrahend by shading
circles in the first ten-frame.

Additional practice can be found in *Practice Your Facts, Levels 1–5,* by Creative Publications.

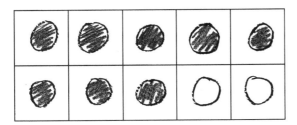

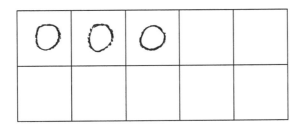

The number of unshaded circles on the first
frame, plus the unshaded circles on the second
the frame, equals the difference between the
two numbers.

$$2 + 3 = 5$$

$$13 - 8 = 5$$

Ten-Between Strategy

Warm-ups

Each warm-up exercise set should take two (2) or three (3) minutes. The short exercise sets are great for filling transition times. Some teachers use them while children stand in line.

Materials

▶ Number cards 0 through 100

▶ Subtraction flash cards

Talk About It

As the children work through these warm-ups, ask them to talk about their thinking. This not only helps you assess, but gives children a chance to clarify their thinking and to hear about ways of thinking that might be different from theirs. You might ask questions like

What strategies help you to know how far a number is from 10?
(The count-back, count-up, fact-families, and think-addition strategies are all helpful in finding the distance from 10.)

To apply the ten-between strategy, what must be true of the two numbers in a subtraction fact?
(One number must be less than ten and the other greater than ten.)

Day 1

Show a number card, for example 14.

What is the difference between 10 and this number?
(4)

Continue with number cards 7 through 13. Show each card at least once.

Extension Show number cards from 17 through 23.

What is the difference between 20 and this number?

Day 2

Show a number card, for example 13.

What is the difference between 10 and this number?

(3)

Continue with number cards 5 through 15. Show each card at least once.

Extension Show number cards 15 through 25.

What is the difference between 20 and this number?

Day 3

Show a number card, for example 16.

What is the difference between 10 and this number?

(6)

Continue with number cards 3 through 17. Show each card at least once.

Extension Show number cards 13 through 27.

What is the difference between 20 and this number?

Day 4

Show a number card, for example 11.

What is the difference between 10 and this number?

(1)

Continue with number cards 0 through 19. Show each card at least once.

Extension Show number cards 10 through 29.

What is the difference between 20 and this number?

Day 5

Show a number card, for example 1.

What two numbers are this far from 10?
(9 and 11)

Repeat with number cards 1 through 3.
Show each card at least once.

Extension Show number cards 1 through 3.

What two numbers are this far from 20?

Day 6

Show a number card, for example 4.

What two numbers are this far from 10?
(6 and 14)

Repeat with number cards 1 through 5.
Show each card at least once.

Extension Show number cards 1 through 5.

What two numbers are this far from 20?

Day 7

Show a number card, for example 7.

What two numbers are this far from 10?
(3 and 17)

Repeat with number cards 1 through 7.
Show each card at least once.

Extension Show number cards from 1
through 7.

What two numbers are this far from 20?

Day 8

Show a number card, for example 8.

What two numbers are this far from 10?
(2 and 18)

Repeat with number cards 1 through 9. Show
each card at least once.

Extension Show number cards 1 through 9.

What two numbers are this far from 20?

Day 9

Show a subtraction flash card, for example
$17 - 3 = \boxed{}$.

How far is the first number from 10?
(7)

How far is the second number from 10?
(7)

What is the sum of the distances from 10 of these two numbers?
(14)

What is 17 minus 3?
(14)

Show subtraction flash cards in which numbers less than 10 are being subtracted from numbers greater than 10.

Extension Present subtraction flash cards with subtrahends 11 through 19 being subtracted from minuends of 21 through 29.

How far is the first number from 20? How far is the second number from 20? What is the sum of the distances? What is the difference between the two numbers?

Day 10

Show a subtraction flash card, for example
$15 - 8 = \boxed{}$.

How far is the first number from 10?
(5)

How far is the second number from 10?
(2)

What is the sum of the distances?
(7)

What is 15 minus 8?
(7)

Continue with subtraction flash cards showing minuends greater than 10 and subtrahends less than ten.

Extension Present flash cards with minuends from 21 through 29 and subtrahends from 11 through 19.

How far is the first number from 20? How far is the second number from 20? What is the sum of the distances? What is the difference between the numbers?

Number Line Differences

Summary

Children use a number line to find the difference between ten and each of two numbers on opposite sides of ten. They compare the sum of those differences to the difference between the two numbers.

Materials

A copy of Number Line Difference, page 78, for each child

Directions

❶ Draw a number line showing numbers 0 through 20 on the chalkboard.

Suppose we want to find the difference between 13 and 8 using this number line. We start by marking 13 and 8.

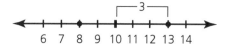

Ten is a friendly number that can help us. How far is 13 from 10?

(3) Show the distance on the number line.

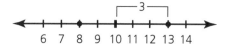

How far is 8 from 10?

(2) Show the distance on the number line.

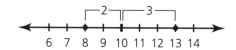

What is the difference between 8 and 13?

(5)

Why?

(Accept any reasonable answer. Illustrate some answers on the number line.)

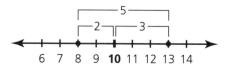

❷ Repeat this activity with other subtraction facts in which the minuend and subtrahend fall on opposite sides of ten.

❸ Distribute copies of Number Line Differences, page 78. Work through the first activity with the children, then have them complete the page on their own.

Talk About It

What is 16 − 7?

(9)

How did find your answer?

(Accept any reasonable answer.)

Did anyone find the answer a different way?

(Accept all methods. The ten-between strategy is not one that all children will choose to use but it is important that they be aware of it. It is also important for children to realize there are many ways to think about finding the answer.)

Extension or Homework

Distribute Number Line Differences #2, page 79. Have children complete the page for additional practice with the ten-between strategy.

Name _____

Number Line Differences #2

Use the number line to find the answers to subtraction facts two ways.

0 1 2 3 4 5 6 7 8 9 10 11 12 13 14 15 16 17 18 19 20

1. Find the difference between 6 and 15.

   What is the distance from 6 to 10? _____ from 15 to 10? _____

   Add the distances. _____ + _____ = _____   Subtract: 15 − 6 = _____

2. Find the difference between 13 and 8.

   What is the distance from 13 to 10? _____ from 8 to 10? _____

   Add the distances. _____ + _____ = _____   Subtract: 13 − 8 = _____

3. Find the difference between 14 and 7.

   What is the distance from 14 to 10? _____ from 7 to 10? _____

   Add the distances. _____ + _____ = _____   Subtract: 14 − 7 = _____

4. Find the difference between 3 and 11.

   What is the distance from 3 to 10? _____ from 11 to 10? _____

   Add the distances. _____ + _____ = _____   Subtract: 11 − 3 = _____

5. Find the difference between 4 and 13.

   What is the distance from 4 to 10? _____ from 13 to 10? _____

   Add the distances. _____ + _____ = _____   Subtract: 13 − 4 = _____

6. Find the difference between 18 and 8.

   What is the distance from 18 to 10? _____ from 8 to 10? _____

   Add the distances. _____ + _____ = _____   Subtract: 18 − 8 = _____

Number Line Differences

Use the number line to find the answers to subtraction facts two ways.

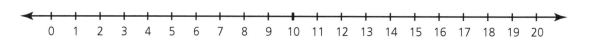

0 1 2 3 4 5 6 7 8 9 10 11 12 13 14 15 16 17 18 19 20

1. Find the difference between 11 and 7.

The distance from 11 to 10 is _____. The distance from 7 to 10 is _____.

Add the distances. _____ + _____ = _____   11 − 7 = _____

2. Find the difference between 12 and 9.

The distance from 12 to 10 is _____. The distance from 9 to 10 is _____.

Add the distances. _____ + _____ = _____   12 − 9 = _____

3. Find the difference between 17 and 8.

The distance from 17 to 10 is _____. The distance from 8 to 10 is _____.

Add the distances. _____ + _____ = _____   17 − 8 = _____

4. Find the difference between 15 and 6.

The distance from 15 to 10 is _____. The distance from 6 to 10 is _____.

Add the distances. _____ + _____ = _____   15 − 6 = _____

5. Find the difference between 14 and 5.

The distance from 14 to 10 is _____. The distance from 5 to 10 is _____.

Add the distances. _____ + _____ = _____   14 − 5 = _____

Number Line Differences #2

Use the number line to find the answers to subtraction facts two ways.

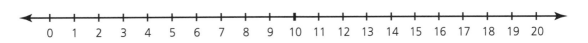

1. Find the difference between 6 and 15.

What is the distance from 6 to 10? _____   from 15 to 10? _____

Add the distances. _____ + _____ = _____   Subtract: 15 − 6 = _____

2. Find the difference between 13 and 8.

What is the distance from 13 to 10? _____   from 8 to 10? _____

Add the distances. _____ + _____ = _____   Subtract: 13 − 8 = _____

3. Find the difference between 14 and 7.

What is the distance from 14 to 10? _____   from 7 to 10? _____

Add the distances. _____ + _____ = _____   Subtract: 14 − 7 = _____

4. Find the difference between 3 and 11.

What is the distance from 3 to 10? _____   from 11 to 10? _____

Add the distances. _____ + _____ = _____   Subtract: 11 − 3 = _____

5. Find the difference between 4 and 13.

What is the distance from 4 to 10? _____   from 13 to 10? _____

Add the distances. _____ + _____ = _____   Subtract: 13 − 4 = _____

6. Find the difference between 18 and 8.

What is the distance from 18 to 10? _____   from 8 to 10? _____

Add the distances. _____ + _____ = _____   Subtract: 18 − 8 = _____

Ten-Between Strategy

Practice

Work on these sets of practice exercises until children can get each answer within three (3) seconds. Ask children to state the entire fact rather than just the answer. Stating the complete fact improves students' recall. Present the facts in various ways. Ask the children to listen and then reply verbally, or use flash cards and have the children write their facts. Varying the format helps all children focus on the facts.

Talk About It

Encourage children to talk about their thinking. Follow up by asking if anyone has a different way to find an answer. You might ask questions like:

How do you determine how far a number is from 10?
(Count up or count down.)

Why can't the ten-between strategy be used in a problem such as 9 − 7?
(The number 10 is not between 7 and 9.)

Can you show how the ten-between strategy works on a number line?

Day 1

Present these facts.

12 − 7 (5)	11 − 7 (4)
13 − 10 (3)	12 − 10 (2)
11 − 8 (3)	13 − 8 (5)
10 − 7 (3)	11 − 9 (2)
13 − 9 (4)	10 − 9 (1)
11 − 10 (1)	13 − 7 (6)
12 − 8 (4)	12 − 9 (3)
10 − 8 (2)	

Extension Present facts with minuends from 20 through 23 and subtrahends from 17 through 20.

Day 2

Present these facts.

14 − 8 (6)	11 − 5 (6)
15 − 7 (8)	14 − 7 (7)
13 − 6 (7)	13 − 8 (5)
12 − 8 (4)	11 − 7 (4)
15 − 9 (6)	12 − 9 (3)
14 − 6 (8)	14 − 5 (9)
13 − 9 (4)	15 − 8 (7)
12 − 5 (7)	13 − 7 (6)
11 − 8 (3)	12 − 6 (6)
15 − 6 (9)	11 − 9 (2)

Extension Present facts with minuends from 20 through 25 and subtrahends from 15 through 20.

Day 3

Present these facts.

16 − 7 (9)	14 − 6 (8)
14 − 9 (5)	17 − 9 (8)
13 − 4 (9)	11 − 3 (8)
12 − 7 (5)	12 − 4 (8)
15 − 6 (9)	16 − 8 (8)
17 − 8 (9)	13 − 7 (6)
16 − 9 (7)	15 − 8 (7)
13 − 5 (8)	14 − 5 (9)
12 − 3 (9)	13 − 9 (4)
11 − 4 (7)	11 − 6 (5)

Extension Present facts that have a difference of 9 or less. Use minuends from 20 through 27 and subtrahends from 13 through 20.

Day 4

Present these facts.

17 − 9 (8)	14 − 7 (7)
11 − 2 (9)	13 − 8 (5)
15 − 9 (6)	12 − 5 (7)
14 − 8 (6)	13 − 7 (6)
13 − 6 (7)	15 − 8 (7)
16 − 7 (9)	11 − 3 (8)
12 − 8 (4)	12 − 7 (5)
11 − 4 (7)	16 − 8 (8)
17 − 8 (9)	15 − 6 (9)
11 − 5 (6)	14 − 5 (9)

Extension Present facts that have a difference of 9 or less. Use minuends from 20 through 29 and subtrahends from 11 through 20.

Day 5

Present these facts.

11 − 8 (3)	17 − 9 (8)
15 − 7 (8)	14 − 7 (7)
12 − 9 (3)	15 − 9 (6)
14 − 6 (8)	12 − 3 (9)
13 − 9 (4)	13 − 4 (9)
17 − 8 (9)	11 − 6 (5)
16 − 9 (7)	16 − 7 (9)
18 − 9 (9)	14 − 5 (9)
12 − 8 (4)	12 − 6 (6)
13 − 7 (6)	11 − 4 (7)

Extension Present facts that have a difference of 9 or less. Use minuends from 21 through 25 and subtrahends from 16 through 19.

Day 6

Present these facts.

15 − 8 (7)	14 − 8 (6)
14 − 9 (5)	13 − 5 (8)
13 − 8 (5)	17 − 8 (9)
17 − 9 (8)	11 − 5 (6)
11 − 7 (4)	12 − 7 (5)
12 − 5 (7)	13 − 6 (7)
16 − 7 (9)	16 − 9 (7)
11 − 9 (2)	15 − 7 (8)
15 − 6 (9)	11 − 3 (8)
12 − 4 (8)	18 − 9 (9)

Extension Present facts with minuends of 31–35, subtrahends of 26–29, and differences 9 or less. Have children count the distance from 30 to numbers on either side of 30 and add the distances together.

Day 7

Present these facts.

11 − 6 (5)	12 − 9 (3)
13 − 5 (8)	13 − 8 (5)
14 − 9 (5)	11 − 7 (4)
15 − 7 (8)	16 − 9 (7)
12 − 5 (7)	14 − 6 (8)
16 − 8 (8)	12 − 7 (5)
11 − 3 (8)	11 − 8 (3)
14 − 7 (7)	17 − 8 (9)
15 − 6 (9)	13 − 4 (9)
17 − 9 (8)	18 − 9 (9)

Extension Present facts with minuends of 41–45, subtrahends 36–39, and differences 9 or less. Have children count the distance from 40 to numbers on either side of 40 and add the distances together.

Day 8

Present these facts.

12 − 8 (4)	17 − 9 (8)
15 − 9 (6)	12 − 4 (8)
13 − 7 (6)	11 − 9 (2)
11 − 4 (7)	13 − 9 (4)
14 − 5 (9)	14 − 8 (6)
16 − 7 (9)	16 − 9 (7)
18 − 9 (9)	17 − 8 (9)
11 − 5 (6)	13 − 6 (7)
12 − 6 (6)	11 − 2 (9)
15 − 8 (7)	12 − 3 (9)

Extension Present facts with minuends of 51–55, subtrahends 46–49, and differences of 9 or less. Have children count the distance from 50 to numbers on either side of 50 and add the distances together.

Day 9

Present these facts.

14 − 9 (5)	13 − 7 (6)
11 − 7 (4)	11 − 6 (5)
15 − 6 (9)	13 − 4 (9)
12 − 7 (5)	14 − 6 (8)
16 − 9 (7)	18 − 9 (9)
13 − 5 (8)	12 − 4 (8)
11 − 3 (8)	16 − 7 (9)
12 − 9 (3)	17 − 9 (8)
17 − 8 (9)	14 − 5 (9)
15 − 9 (6)	11 − 4 (7)

Extension Present facts with minuends of 61–65, subtrahends of 56–59, and differences of 9 or less. Have children count the distance from 60 to numbers on either side of 60 and add the distances together.

Day 10

Present these facts.

12 − 3 (9)	16 − 7 (9)
15 − 8 (7)	13 − 8 (5)
13 − 6 (7)	12 − 7 (5)
11 − 2 (9)	11 − 9 (2)
14 − 7 (7)	15 − 7 (8)
17 − 8 (9)	18 − 9 (9)
13 − 9 (4)	14 − 5 (9)
11 − 5 (6)	17 − 9 (8)
12 − 6 (6)	11 − 8 (3)
14 − 8 (6)	16 − 9 (7)

Extension Present facts with minuends of 71–75, subtrahends of 66–69, and differences of 9 or less. Have children count the distances from 70 to numbers on either side of 70 and add those distances together.

Subtraction Chart

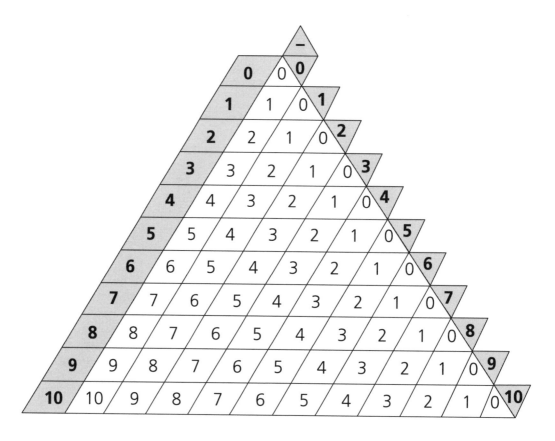

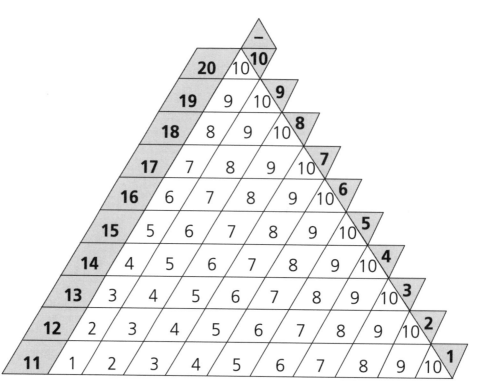

© Creative Publications 32311

Subtraction Chart

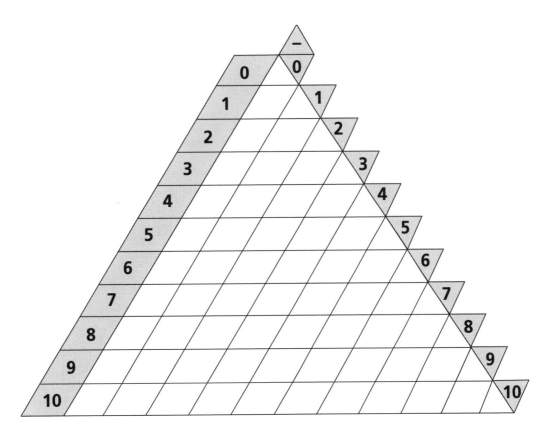

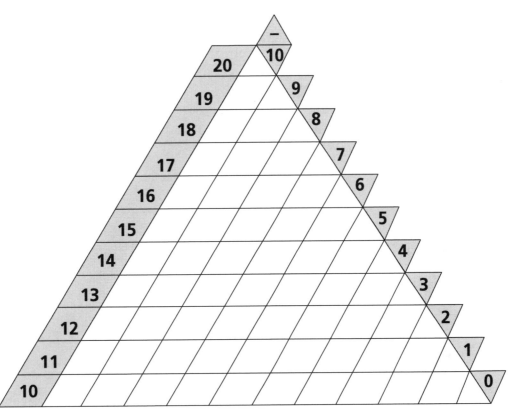

Addition Chart

+	0	1	2	3	4	5	6	7	8	9	10
0	0	1	2	3	4	5	6	7	8	9	10
1	1	2	3	4	5	6	7	8	9	10	11
2	2	3	4	5	6	7	8	9	10	11	12
3	3	4	5	6	7	8	9	10	11	12	13
4	4	5	6	7	8	9	10	11	12	13	14
5	5	6	7	8	9	10	11	12	13	14	15
6	6	7	8	9	10	11	12	13	14	15	16
7	7	8	9	10	11	12	13	14	15	16	17
8	8	9	10	11	12	13	14	15	16	17	18
9	9	10	11	12	13	14	15	16	17	18	19
10	10	11	12	13	14	15	16	17	18	19	20

Addition Chart

+	0	1	2	3	4	5	6	7	8	9	10
0											
1											
2											
3											
4											
5											
6											
7											
8											
9											
10											

Bibliography

Practice Your Facts. Chicago, Creative Publications, Inc., 1999. These 80-page practice books offer traditional practice on basic facts for all four operations.

Holden, Linda, and Micaelia Brummett Randolph. *Understanding Addition & Subtraction.* Chicago, Creative Publications, Inc., 1988. Forty-eight carefully sequenced, reproducible lessons help children make connections between concrete experiences, pictorial representations, and abstract equations. The 128-page binder includes activities using linking cubes and counting chips.

Irvine, Rhea, and Kathryn Walker. *Smart Arithmetic, Grades 1–3.* Chicago, Creative Publications, Inc., 1995. This 96-page teacher resource book helps you guide your children in a thinking approach to computation as they invent their own algorithms. A start-up bank of suggested activities provides experiences in discourse, visual thinking, mental computation, and fact recall.

Leutzinger, Larry. *Facts That Last: A Balanced Approach to Memorization.* Chicago, Creative Publications, Inc., 1999. This series of four books, one for each operation, employs fact strategies to make memorizing facts easy. Teach your children a handful of strategies and watch them accurately speed through fact acquisition. These 96-page books include hands-on activities and practice.

National Council of Teachers of Mathematics. *Standards 2000 Draft.* Reston, Virginia, 2000. This document emphasizes the importance of mastering basic facts. Indeed, fast and accurate recall of basic facts is an essential tool in the mathematical toolkit.

Pittock, Janet, and Ann Roper. *Practice Worth Repeating.* Chicago, Creative Publications, Inc., 1999. Help children keep their fact recall fast and accurate with enjoyable practice. These manageable 32-page books include several engaging practice activities that can be used over and over with the same children.

Ward, Sandra. *Constructing Ideas About Number Combinations.* Chicago, Creative Publications, Inc., 1995. Fourteen one- to five-day explorations help children construct and deepen their understanding of addition and subtraction. Each exploration is clearly presented in an easy to use format and includes reproducible homework. 112 pages.

Larry Leutzinger, author of the *Facts That Last* series, is an associate professor at the University of Northern Iowa and co-director of the Iowa Mathematics and Science Coalition. Dr. Leutzinger's major interests include teaching mental mathematics concepts, including basic facts, to pre-K through fourth grade students. He is actively researching the knowledge and abilities of those students.